Who I Am
and
Who I Want to Be

E. Richard Churchill
and
Linda R. Churchill

J. Weston Walch, Publisher
Portland, Maine

1   2   3   4   5   6   7   8   9   10

ISBN 0-8251-2211-2

Copyright © 1992
J. Weston Walch, Publisher
P.O. Box 658 • Portland, Maine 04104-0658

Printed in the United States of America

Contents

1
Who I Am

You are you. That's who you are. That's who you've always been. Everyone knows that.

But exactly who are you?

Let's take time to discover exactly who you are. Once you know exactly who you are, it will be time to explore how you can best deal with the person you are. Then you can begin to describe the person you *want* to be.

To begin with, you're special. You are unique. You're the only person in the world who is exactly like you in all ways. Even if you're a twin, you're the only person exactly like you. No matter how much you look and act like someone else, you're still different in many ways from any other human on earth. That's what makes you special. You're one of a kind. You're *you*!

What makes you special? In what ways are you unique?

No one in the world looks quite like you. When you smile or frown or laugh or cry, you look different from anyone else. That's because you look just like you. When your eyes light up at a joke or because of something funny that has just happened, they give you a look which is yours and yours alone. The same thing is true when your face clouds in sadness.

When you write your name, it is *your* handwriting and no one else's that flows from the point of your pen or pencil. When you speak or shout or whisper, the voice others hear is your voice. It belongs to you.

The manner in which you react to things that happen or what people say or do is specially yours. What makes you laugh or cry or shout or sing may be the same things which cause others to laugh or cry or shout or sing, but your voice and expression will be uniquely yours. That's because you're you. You are different from anyone else in the world.

You have thoughts and emotions that are not exactly like those of anyone else. Ideas that come to you may be similar to those that others have, but you'll always have a special little twist or extra that makes your ideas just a bit different.

The way you feel about things is your way of feeling. Those things which make others happy or sad may cause you to feel the same way. But your feelings of joy or sorrow will always be your feelings. Your happiness is never exactly the same as another's because of all your past experiences and hopes for the future. When you experience sadness it is a different sadness from the one anyone else feels from the same causes.

You can do things no one else can. Sometimes you'll do them better. At times you'll be less capable than other people. You'll always use your abilities in a manner which is yours and yours alone. You have special talents you may not yet have discovered. When you do they will be different than the talents of anyone else. That's because they are yours and you are a very special person.

You are different from all other people. Though you are much like many people you are unlike everyone except yourself. This is what makes you who you are.

Since you are different and unique you will become someone who may be similiar to but will never be exactly like anyone else. Who you want to be depends a lot upon who you are now and how you make use of all those thousands of abilities and qualities which make you special.

Let's begin by finding out who you are right now. Once you know exactly who you are you can begin to explore how this will enable you to become the very special person you want to be.

A Quick Look At Me

Begin by filling in the following facts which help describe who you are. These things help tell about you as a physical person.

My name is _____

My home address is _____

in the city of _____ in the state of _____

My telephone number is _____

I am _____ years and _____ months old and was born on

the following date. _____

I'm _____ feet and _____ inches tall and weigh

_____ pounds.

My hair color is _____ and the color of my eyes is

_____ .

I'm in _____ grade at _____ school.

I have _____ brothers and sisters whose names are:

_____

_____

I live with these adults: _____

_____

_____

Here are three or more facts about the physical person I am (are you right-handed, do you wear glasses, is your hair curly?).

_____

_____

_____

More About Myself

You are more than merely a physical person. You are a thinking human being with ideas, likes, dislikes, and all sorts of plans and hopes. Let's take a look at some of the mental and emotional things which help make you the person you are at this very moment.

Do you have a job? _____   If so, what sort of work do you do and how many hours do you work each week?

_____

_____

If you don't have a job, what sort of part-time work might you be able to do while you are still in school?

_____

_____

What hobbies or activities do you have at present?

_____

_____

Are there hobbies or activities you would like to take part in if you had the time, the money, or special abilities necessary to enjoy them? What are they?

_____

_____

Who are three of your best or closest friends?

_____

_____

Which are your three favorite television shows?

_____

_____

Name two classes or subjects you enjoy more than the others in school.

_____

_____

What three things would you like for every teacher to know or understand about you?

_____

_____

_____

What three things would you like for your friends to know or understand about you?

_____

_____

We all admire or look up to certain people. Who do you most admire or look up to? Who is your hero or heroine?

_____

What is it about this person which causes you to admire and look up to her or him?

_____

_____

Look back over the information you have just written about things, activities, and people. What you've written should tell you quite a bit about what you like and enjoy. Finish this section by naming three things you enjoy in life which you did not list above. In just a few words tell how each item you list helps describe the sort of person you are. (For example, "I enjoy hikes and bike rides but only with other people. I like outdoor exercise but don't like to be alone.")

1. _____

_____

2. _____

_____

3. _____

_____

My Personal Pennant

Going back to the Middle Ages, families often had flags, crests, and pennants that told others something of their family's history. These items also told others what the family stood for in terms of loyalty, honesty, and the like.

When knights rode into battle, their shields often were painted with the family symbols. This helped identify the knight both to friends and foes and also gave him a feeling of representing his family in battle.

There were certain symbols on flags, pennants, and crests that generally meant the same thing. For example, lions usually were a sign of bravery. A cross indicated a strong religious belief.

Colors also stood for certain things. Red might represent bravery or blood, while blue stood for water or sky. Yellow could indicate sun or fields of ripe grain.

You're going to design a personal pennant that will tell something about you. The symbols you choose will be up to you. Just select symbols that represent what you want to say about yourself.

In the upper left corner of your pennant, draw symbols that tell about your early childhood. (If you moved around a lot, a car might show this fact. A dog or cat could symbolize the fact that a pet was important to you.)

Use the upper right corner of the pennant for symbols representing your first three or four years in school. (A happy mask might indicate you liked school, or a bus could represent the fact you rode to and from school.)

In the lower left corner, draw symbols that show your present time of life. (Athletic equipment may indicate your favorite sport, just as a book or TV set can show a way you spend leisure time.)

Finally, use the lower right corner of your personal pennant to depict what you anticipate being important in your life during the next two or three years. (A report card could indicate good grades and a work scene might show a part-time job.)

If you wish, color your pennant. Choose colors that best represent the things you feel are important in your life.

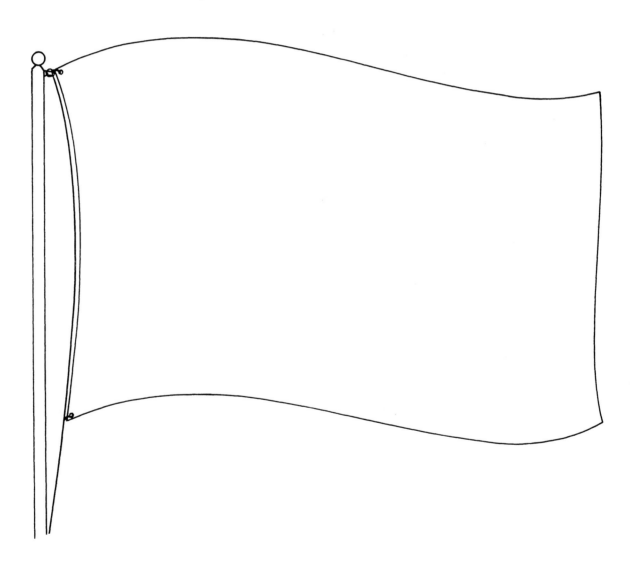

The Younger Me

Things which have already happened have a lot to do with the person you are today. Experiences and adventures, toys and possessions, friends and family have all helped shape the person you have become.

Take time to look back at yourself when you were younger. Let's think about some things which were important to you as a young child. Even though you may not realize it, many of these things were important in causing you to grow into the person you are at this moment.

 Most children have a favorite toy. What was your favorite toy when you were younger?

_____

_____

How did playing with this toy help you physically, or mentally, or emotionally?

_____

_____

What was the single thing of which you were proudest when you were a young child? This may have been a possession (such as your favorite toy), a member of your family, or perhaps something you did.

_____

_____

What was it that caused you to have so much pride in this?

_____

_____

Most children have a nickname when they are young. What was yours?

_____

_____

How did you feel about that nickname?

_____

_____

Young children do and say silly things. What was the silliest thing you did or said when you were younger?

_____

_____

Because of their lack of experience in the world, young children do and say things they later think of as stupid. If you had to choose one thing you did or said when you were younger which seems really stupid now, what would it be?

_____

_____

When they are young, children have a way of doing and saying things which are extremely funny without being silly. What's your first choice for the funniest thing which you did or said or which happened to you as you were growing up?

_____

_____

Life isn't always a bed of roses for young children. They lose things that they treasure. Sometimes the loss is a prized possession. It may be a friend or family member. Looking back on your childhood, what do you see now as your most important loss?

_____

_____

Fear may be a very real part of the lives of young children. Some children fear physical things such as "bad people," the dark, or emergency sirens. Others are afraid of more emotional things such as getting lost or being left behind. What were your worst fears when you were young?

_____

_____

Very young children feel they are the center of the universe. It is as they mature that children begin to learn to share love and attention. As we grow up we also gain the ability to look back at our younger years and see ourselves as others might have seen us.

Write ten words your parents might have used (and perhaps did use) in describing you between the ages of four and ten. Consider such descriptive words as kind, pretty, spoiled, generous, selfish, etc.

_____

_____

A Few of My Favorite Things

In *The Sound of Music,* Maria sings about some of her favorite things. Favorite things not only help to make life enjoyable, they also give you a clue as to what sort of person you are.

Consider what items are your very favorite things in each of the following categories.

Holiday _____

Animal _____

Food _____

Season of the year _____

Sport or game to play _____

Athlete _____

Store to shop in _____

Footwear _____

Type of clothing _____

Hair cut or style _____

Music group _____

Car _____

Color when you're sad _____

Color when you're happy _____

Place to hang out _____

Time of day _____

Film or television star _____

Place or person to visit _____

Thing to do _____

Designing a T-Shirt That Is Me

We wear T-shirts that tell a lot about ourselves. Our T-shirts may feature our favorite NFL team, a rock group whose concert we recently attended, or a product we enjoy using. Prized T-shirts for many of us are those we earned from taking part in an activity such as a fun run, a swimming meet, a bike tour, or a sports tournament. Other popular T-shirts depict a city, country, or famous site we've visited.

We also enjoy wearing T-shirts with printed messages that make a statement for us. Often such shirts have part of the message on the front and the rest on the back.

Use the outlines on page 12 to design the front and back of two T-shirts, or the front only of four T-shirts.

I Am Bugged By . . .

No matter how smoothly life goes there are always some things that annoy every one of us. You are not an exception. There are some events, certain situations, and a few people who really bug you. At times you can ignore these things or at least pretend to ignore them. Sometimes it's possible to remedy a situation so it no longer bugs you.

But what about those places, times, and people who can't be ignored and are impossible to change?

Identifying the things you are bugged by is one more way of finding out exactly who you are. Listing these bugging items gets them out in the open. You'll find some satisfaction in just writing them down.

In each of the four "bugs" that follow, write a short description of something that really bugs you.

Bear with Me

Now that you've looked at yourself to find what things really bug you, it's time to do a different self-evaluation. This time you're going to take a look at yourself to see what things you do and say which may give others a bad impression.

Once you've discovered something about yourself that may very well bother others, you may want to think about how to change so that you no longer annoy those about you.

Since change does not always occur overnight, it will take some time for you to alter things about yourself that cause others to be bugged by you. While you're working on change you can hope your friends and family will bear with you.

In each bear on page 15, describe something you've discovered about yourself which really does need to be improved or changed. You might even add a few words telling how you plan to work on this improvement or change.

Discovered Me

By now you've thought and written quite a bit about who you are. You've probably discovered some things about yourself you hadn't thought of before.

Let's finish up this first section by writing a simple little poem which will summarize some of the things you have recently found out about yourself.

Follow the line-by-line instructions to create an eight-line poem which will be different from any other poem ever written. That's because it will be about you, and you are special because you're the only person in the world exactly like you.

Write or finish each line in your poem according to the directions. Remember, poems don't have to rhyme in order to be poetry.

Begin your poem by writing your first name on line one.

On the second line write four adjectives (words such as happy, intelligent, pretty, etc.) which describe the way you feel about yourself.

Line three tells something about your family. You might begin it, 'Son/daughter of . . .' or 'Brother/sister of . . .'.

Use the fourth line to name three things you really enjoy. Just finish off the line which is already started for you.

Complete the fifth line, which is already begun, by telling how you feel about three things.

Finish the sixth line by naming three things you'd like to have happen.

For the seventh line give three things that frighten you.

Write your last name on the final line and your poem is complete.

1. _____

2. _____

3. _____

4. *One who enjoys* _____

_____

5. *Who feels* _____

_____

6. *Who'd like to see* _____

_____

7. *Whose fears include* _____

_____

8. _____

2
How I See Me

Did you know you may see yourself differently than others see you? In order to know who you really are, it's important to take time to discover how you see yourself. The way you view yourself has a great deal to do with how you live your life. It affects what you think, how you act, what you say, and even how you feel.

When you see yourself as a good person, we say you have a *positive feeling* about yourself. When you think bad things about yourself or your actions, you have *negative feelings*.

Positive feelings give you a good self-concept. You have high self-esteem when most of your feelings about yourself are positive. The better your self-concept is, the better you feel. When you feel good about yourself, you are a happy person.

Negative feelings can cause you to feel you have little worth and are a bad person. These feelings lower your self-concept. Negative feelings can cause you to feel sad or depressed.

You can't feel good all the time. All of us experience times of unhappiness. However, the better you feel about yourself, the happier you will be. Positive feelings help make for a good self-concept.

In this chapter you're going to take a long look at the way you see yourself. By the time you finish the chapter, you'll have a good idea exactly why you see yourself the way you do.

A Survey of My Attitudes

A first step in discovering how you see yourself is to take a survey of your attitudes. Respond to each of the following statements by circling the code which *best* describes you.

If you agree with a statement, circle the letter A at the right. When you disagree with a statement, circle the letter D. If you can't decide how you feel about a statement, circle CD.

1. I can tell my friends my feelings.   A   D   CD

2. I can talk easily with people I don't know.   A   D   CD

3. I can express my feelings and thoughts when I am part of a group.   A   D   CD

4. I feel comfortable introducing myself to people I've just met.   A   D   CD

5. I can accept a compliment when it is given.   A   D   CD

6. I am aware of my weaknesses.   A   D   CD

7. I can listen to others and understand their feelings.   A   D   CD

8. I get upset easily.   A   D   CD

9. I am unaware of my strong points.   A   D   CD

10. I can keep secrets.   A   D   CD

11. The students in this school are warm and friendly to me.   A   D   CD

12. Most kids aren't really interested in school and learning.   A   D   CD

13. I enjoy giving compliments to people who deserve them.   A   D   CD

14. Most of the time I solve my problems with friends by arguing
    or fighting with them.   A   D   CD

15. I can talk with my teachers when I have problems.   A   D   CD

16. I am proud of my school.   A   D   CD

17. My teachers are warm and friendly.   A   D   CD

18. Our principal really cares about the students.   A   D   CD

19. The counselors have time to listen to my problems.   A   D   CD

20. Our assistant principal deals fairly with us.   A   D   CD

My List of Personal Adjectives

Adjectives are words that describe. Since you're going to be using words that describe you as a person, these words will be *personal adjectives.*

Here are some pleasant or positive personal adjectives that people might use to describe themselves:

confident	reliable	kind	lucky	cheerful
courageous	energetic	calm	clever	relaxed
content	loving	sensitive	concerned	interested
curious	eager	earnest	bold	secure

Here are some negative personal adjectives:

angry	hateful	depressed	miserable	sulky
uncertain	unsure	lost	tense	alone
useless	pathetic	nervous	scared	suspicious
dejected	hurt	sad	unhappy	bitter

There are hundreds of personal adjectives you might use to describe the way you see yourself. Those listed above should give you some ideas and start you thinking about what adjectives best describe the way you see yourself.

Think of the box on these two pages as your day. You'll move through this "day" from left to right.

early morning

Decide on personal adjectives that describe the various times during your day. Don't limit your choice of adjectives to those in the lists.

Then you'll fill in the day, listing words that describe how you feel in the morning, at noontime, in the afternoon, after school, and in the early and late evening. To see how this works, here are a few possible examples.

- "Tired" might fit in the early morning because you stayed up late the night before and were not ready to get out of bed.
- "Worried" could come in the early morning because of a big math test.
- "Relieved" might come about midday when you've lived through the test.
- "Bored" could describe the way you felt right after lunch when your language arts teacher had to answer questions about things you already knew.
- "Excited" describes your feelings right after the sixth hour when your best friend asked you out for pizza and Cokes.
- "Disgusted" might fit when your seventh hour teacher gave you a big homework assignment.
- "Relieved" might fit again when you finish that assignment.

Now fill the box with your own adjectives.

late evening

Once you've filled the box with adjectives that represent your day, look back over your day. As you read the adjectives you've written for various parts of the day, answer these questions:

What time or times during the day do I seem to be in the best

mood? _____

_____

At what times do I seem able to do my best work? _____

_____

_____

Are there times when I appear dejected or moody? When are

these times? _____

_____

_____

Are there times when I want to be alone? When? _____

_____

_____

When do I seem at my best around other people? _____

_____

_____

What other general statements can you make about yourself

when you look back over the adjective box? _____

_____

_____

_____

_____

_____

I See Me As a Unique Person

We are all unique. No person is exactly like any other person. Take a look at yourself and decide what special qualities make you unique. Perhaps it's your ability to do something athletically that others can't. Maybe it is your sense of humor or your ability to tell a good joke. You may be able to make others feel comfortable when you first meet them.

Look closely enough at yourself to see what makes you truly unique.

You may be larger or smaller than others in your class. Other than physical size, what are two or three physical things about you that make you different from other people?

_____

_____

You may be one of the mentally swiftest members of your class or among the less-rapid thinkers. No matter where you stand on the class mental ladder, there are things about your mind and the way you think that are different from all others in the class. Explain how your mind works in two or three ways that make you truly unique among the members of your class.

_____

_____

_____

The way you look and dress adds to your uniqueness. Give two or three things about your appearance that set you apart from the crowd.

_____

_____

_____

There's an old saying that tells us actions speak louder than words. In what ways do your actions help prove you are a totally unique individual?

_____

_____

_____

When you talk with friends, when you meet strangers, and when you encounter people you know, you act in ways that help you relate to people. Describe two or three ways you act toward people that help make you different from others.

_____

_____

_____

Glance back over the things you have just discovered that help make you unique. What one thing about you is the most important when it comes to making you truly your own person who is different from all others?

_____

_____

_____

Match Up

In the first part of this exercise, you will be looking only at yourself. Let's begin by considering some things you like and dislike.

List one item you like and another you dislike for each of the categories on the next page. Don't spend a lot of time worrying about your choices. Just try to pick one thing you really like and another you really dislike for each category.

	LIKE	DISLIKE
Football team	_____	_____
Car	_____	_____
TV program	_____	_____
Musical group	_____	_____
Movie or TV actor or actress	_____	_____
School subject	_____	_____
Chore at home	_____	_____
Food	_____	_____
Color	_____	_____

To complete the first part of this project, think of some enjoyable experiences you have had. List two of the best experiences you have ever had.

_____

_____

Life isn't always fun. Not all experiences are enjoyable. List two things you have experienced that were not at all enjoyable. They probably were either frightening or sad.

_____

_____

_____

Now for the second part of Match-Up. Get together with another person in the class to compare your responses. Keep track of the number of times the two of you agree on things you like and dislike. Then check to see if you share any experiences you both enjoyed or both found unenjoyable.

You'll probably discover that the two of you share some likes and dislikes. You'll also note you have different views on other points. This is to be expected.

You are unique because you are not entirely like anyone else. However, you have some of the same qualities as others.

If you wish, compare your ideas with more than one person in class. You may be surprised to discover that someone you know well lists different likes and dislikes than you expect.

The Perfect Me Place

Think about designing a room that would be absolutely perfect for you. It might be a bedroom with plenty of room for everything you'd like to have handy. Your perfect Me Place might be a den or library. It could be a workshop or laboratory filled with all the tools and equipment necessary to make the sorts of projects you'd love to construct.

Begin by deciding how large your perfect place would be. Write the dimensions along the outside of the box on the next page. If the shape given is not the perfect shape for what you are planning, use a pen and ruler to change the box to the shape you prefer.

Decide where to place doors and windows and then locate them in the drawing. What pieces of furniture would you like to have in your perfect room?

Remember to design enough closet and storage space to hold all the things you have or would like to have.

Don't forget things such as a computer and perhaps a television set. Remember to include a CD player and stereo system if you wish.

Think about how to arrange your Me Place so that everything is exactly where it should be to make the location the perfect place for you.

I'm Proud of That

Taking pride in things you do and accomplish is an indication you've done well. There are probably many things you've done that cause you to feel proud.

There may be many more things that you should be proud about. It may surprise you to realize just how many things you should take pride in.

Let's take a close look at you and see if you can discover a number of things that should cause you to be proud of yourself.

Supply at least one example for each of the following statements. As you work on this exercise, you may be amazed at the variety of things of which you should be proud.

1. I am proud of something I am able to do on my own without help from adults.

   _____

   _____

2. I am proud of a new skill I recently learned.

   _____

   _____

3. At school I recently did something of which I am proud.

   _____

   _____

4. I made a decision that took a lot of thought but made me proud of myself.

   _____

   _____

5. Not too long ago I said something that still gives me pride.

_____

_____

6. I am proud of myself for a decision I made regarding money.

_____

_____

7. I am proud that I worked hard to overcome or change a habit or attitude.

_____

_____

8. Once I spoke out when I could have kept silent. Now I am proud that I did.

_____

_____

9. My family has a tradition of which I am really proud.

_____

_____

10. I'm proud that I finished a job that others might have given up on.

_____

_____

11. I am proud that I did something that helped someone else feel better.

_____

_____

12. I've done at least one thing I'm proud of that helps our ecology or environment.

_____

_____

13. I'm proud of a family member because of the way that person lives his or her life.

_____

_____

14. One time I did not go along with the group and I'm proud I did not.

_____

_____

15. I am proud that I've done something to make my community a better place in which to live.

_____

_____

16. I'm proud of myself for not saying something I considered saying.

_____

_____

17. I wrote something which makes me proud.

_____

_____

18. I can take pride in something I made or helped build.

_____

_____

19. By helping my family I've done something of which I am proud.

_____

_____

_____

20. I've done something to please myself that I take pride in.

_____

_____

_____

New Directions

Certain events in our lives start us in a new direction. After we start in that new direction, our lives are changed forever. For example, when you started school your life took a new direction. The birth of a younger brother or sister gave you a new direction in life. Moving to a new community, meeting someone who became your special friend, or making a team are all examples of new directions your life may have taken.

Pick one new direction that has been important to your life. Write a short story about taking that new direction. Simply describe what happened and tell how you happened to be involved in taking that new direction. (Use the next page to continue your story.)

_____

_____

_____

_____

_____

_____

_____

_____

_____

_____

_____

_____

_____

_____

After taking a new direction, your life changes from the way it has been before. Sometimes the change is good. At other times such change may be bad.

In the space below, illustrate how your life changed because of the new direction you just wrote about. You may make one drawing or a series of drawings. If you don't feel you are a good artist, feel free to draw simple stick figures to illustrate this change.

Sometimes I'm Strong and Sometimes I'm Weak

We all have strengths and weaknesses. You know you're better at some things than at others. Begin by deciding whether each of the following is one of your strong points or is a weak area. Write an "S" after an item to show you are strong in that area. Write a "W" for those areas in which you are weak.

Art _____   Music _____

Sports _____   Reading _____

Science _____   Math _____

Spelling _____   Handwriting _____

English usage _____   Social studies _____

Now let's look at some personal traits. Use the same "S" and "W" rating system.

I try to be on time. _____   I'm well organized. _____

I pay attention. _____   I finish tasks. _____

I take care of my things. _____   I work on my own. _____

People can depend on me. _____   I take responsibility. _____

I am honest. _____   I exercise self-control. _____

What are your three most important strong points? Describe them. They may or may not be among those points you rated yourself on above.

1. _____

  _____

2. _____

  _____

3. _____

  _____

Choose three things about yourself you would like to work on to change and make better. They don't have to be from the items you just rated.

1. _____

  _____

  _____

  _____

2. _____

  _____

  _____

  _____

3. _____

  _____

Life Isn't Always Happy

There are times in life when you aren't happy. Sadness is part of living. Certain sounds and sights can cause you to be sad for a few seconds or a minute or two. Let's begin by checking to see what can cause you to have a bit of momentary sadness.

Complete the following statements:

1. I have a feeling of sadness when I hear the sound of

_____ .

2. When I smell _____ I may feel sad.

3. I feel momentarily sad when I see _____ .

4. The feel of _____ can make me feel sad.

Things other than hearing, smelling, seeing, or feeling certain things can cause sadness. List other experiences that may cause you to feel sad for a time.

_____

_____

_____

_____

_____

_____

_____

_____

We all have events or days that stand out in our lives as being extremely sad. Sometimes the things that caused sadness happened to us or to members of our families. At times the events or experiences touched someone we knew. Learning about the divorce of your best friend's parents can make you sad, so can finding out someone you know has **AIDS**.

Decide on what was one of the saddest events or days in your life. Write a short story about that event or day.

_____

_____

_____

_____

_____

_____

_____

_____

_____

_____

_____

_____

_____

_____

_____

_____

_____

_____

_____

It's Great to Be Happy

Nearly everyone agrees it is more fun to be happy than to be sad. It can be said we appreciate happy times more because of the sad times we have had.

There are certain sights and sounds that you associate with happiness. Let's start by having you recall some things that usually make you happy.

Complete these statements:

1. Whenever I hear the sound of _____ , I find myself feeling happy.

2. The scent of _____ causes me to be happy.

3. The taste of _____ makes me happy.

4. I feel happy when I see _____ .

Naturally, other things nearly always trigger a feeling of happiness for you. Tell about some other things that make you feel happy.

_____

_____

_____

_____

It is fun to remember happy times and pleasant experiences. If you were going to choose the single most happy time or experience in your life, what would it be? Write a description of the happiest day or event in your life.

_____

_____

_____

_____

How I Deal with My Anger

It is perfectly normal to become angry from time to time. The important thing is not to allow anger to get out of control.

Not everyone becomes angry about the same things. What may cause one person to become extremely angry may only cause another a shake of the head and a weary smile.

What are three things that cause you to become extremely upset or angry?

1. _____

_____

2. _____

_____

3. _____

_____

People deal with anger in different ways. Some of us shout and wave our arms when we are angry. Others become absolutely silent. Some people try to hold their anger in, while others let everyone know how upset they are.

How do you handle your anger? What do you do and say when you are very upset?

_____

_____

_____

_____

Becoming angry is different from losing your temper. You can be angry but remain under control. Loss of temper is also a loss of some of your self-control. What can cause you to lose your temper?

_____

_____

_____

_____

We all have said and done things we later wish had never happened. Often anger causes events like this. Think back to one time you became angry and let your anger cause you to do or say something you now wish had not happened.

Write a short account of what caused you to become so angry at that time. Tell what you did or said as a result of your anger. Finish your account by suggesting how you might have better handled the problem.

_____

_____

_____

_____

_____

_____

_____

_____

_____

_____

_____

_____

A Letter to Me

In this chapter you have taken a close look at yourself. You should have a good idea of how you see yourself. You are aware of things you like and things that bother you. You have thought about what makes you happy or sad and things in which you can take pride.

As you've thought about the projects in this chapter, you have considered how you might change or improve. You have also brought to mind some really good things you've done.

Even though you probably were not always completely pleased with yourself, you did discover something extremely important. You have looked at yourself and found that you are a good person. Most likely you thought about some things you really like about yourself.

You're going to finish this chapter by writing a letter about yourself to yourself. It's a letter from you to you. Tell yourself what you've found out about you. Tell what you value about yourself and what you've discovered that you truly like about you.

3

Managing Me

The way you deal with things is the way you *manage* yourself. How you feel has a lot to do with the manner in which you manage yourself. When you're happy and feeling good about life, you are likely to deal with things one way. Those times you're sad or angry or feeling bad you are likely to manage yourself differently.

Much of how you manage yourself involves deciding what to do, how to accomplish it, and when to do it. This is known as *decision making.*

In order to decide how to manage yourself, you have to do several things. You do these things without thinking about the steps involved.

First, you have to define the problem that needs a decision. After all, you can't decide what to do until you have an idea what needs to be done.

Second, it is necessary to think about all the possible ways to approach the problem. You can't make a good decision until you consider the various things you might possibly do.

The third step in making a decision is to think of your values. You need to ask youself what is important to you.

Now you're ready for the fourth step in deciding how to manage yourself. It's time to think of what can go wrong or what can be right as the result of any choice you make.

Finally, you're ready to decide how to best solve a problem. Simply choose the one type of action that is the best one possible.

Once you've made a decision, you are ready to manage the way you act and live. You're on the road to managing yourself.

Daily Decisions Are a Big Part of Living

You make thousands of decisions every day. This is how you manage your life.

Often it is easy to know immediately whether or not you made the proper decision.

When auto horns honk and the crossing guard screams, you know at once you made a poor decision when you ran across the street when the light was red.

When the umpire yells, "Strike!" and your team members moan, you know at once you should have taken a cut at the ball that just crossed the plate.

But we don't always have instant feedback regarding our decisions. Sometimes it takes days or weeks or even longer before we find out how good or how bad our decisions were.

The time you wrote the nasty note about your friend, you had no idea she would ever find out. Yet, three days later, your friend suddenly stopped speaking to you.

Each day for two weeks you paid just a little less attention in class. Then came the *big test*. Next came your *poor grade* on the test.

Let's look at some decisions you've made recently. Perhaps you made them as recently as today or as long ago as last week.

Describe three decisions you made recently, which you knew almost at once were good or bad.

1. _____

_____

2. _____

_____

3. _____

_____

Within the last few days you've made some decisions that took a bit longer before you knew whether they were right or wrong choices. Describe three decisions whose feedback was not instant.

1. _____

_____

2. _____

_____

3. _____

_____

Unfortunately none of us always makes the best decision. For any of a number of reasons we don't stop to think of all the choices available before deciding. We may not consider all the possible results of a decision. At times we fail to think of our own values before making a final decision.

There are a number of reasons we sometimes fail to make good decisions. We may be angry, tired, or hurried, for example.

Think back to some of the poor decisions you've made. They may be recent or old news. What helped cause you to make these poor choices?

It isn't necessary to describe the decisions. Just try to decide what things contributed to your poor decisions. Describe these things here.

_____

_____

_____

_____

_____

_____

When faced with a difficult decision, many of us try to put off making the hard choice. This is called *procrastinating*. We may procrastinate because it is possible someone else will decide for us. We may put off a difficult decision in hopes we'll get more information. There are any number of reasons some of us put off making decisions that bother us.

What can happen when you put off making a decision? Think about one time you delayed making a decision. Did the delay make things better or worse?

Describe that decision and tell what happened because you held off before making it.

_____

_____

_____

Let's finish this project on a positive note.

What's the best decision you've made in the last twenty-four hours?

_____

Tell about the best decision you ever made in your life.

_____

Solving My Problems

As we've already mentioned, decision-making involves solving problems. You go through the decision-making and problem-solving process many times each day. Or at least you should.

Are you at ease when it comes to making decisions? Or do you find it hard to decide exactly what to do? Does procrastinating sometimes cause the problem to become worse?

Remember, we all have problems that must be solved. You aren't the only person in the world who is faced with decisions. Every possible solution can seem less than perfect. It is in your best interest to find the solution that comes closest to being a good one.

If problem-solving isn't one of your strong points, perhaps a little push in the right direction will improve your ability to make decisions. Take a look at this decision-making diagram. It gives you a visual picture of what you read at the beginning of this chapter.

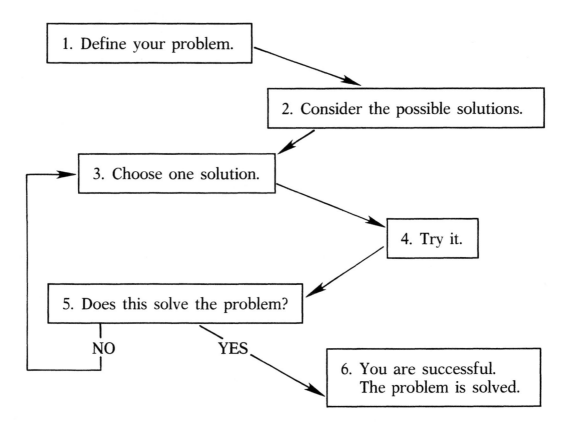

Let's make sure this diagram makes sense to you. Begin by deciding exactly what your problem is. Once you look closely at what needs to be done, you will sometimes realize the solution is simpler than you thought.

How many ways might you be able to solve your problem? Don't be too quick to decide there is only one solution. This often is not true for complicated or involved problems.

Pick what seems to be the best possible solution. Remember, just because one possible solution seems best at first glance, it may not prove to be the best way to deal with a sticky problem. Keep in mind your own values when you select a method of solving a problem.

Try your solution. See if it solves the problem. If so, you've been successful in decision-making and problem-solving.

If your solution does not do the job, then back up to the third step. Choose another way of solving the problem and give it a try. You may have to explore several ideas before you find the one that works for you. Don't get discouraged and give up. Keep trying until you find a workable solution.

Don't let problems stack up until they get you down. Solve them as they appear. No matter how difficult a problem seems, it *will* have a solution. The solution may not make you absolutely happy, but there is a solution you can live with. It's up to you to find that solution.

Learning to Accept Responsibility

Everyone must learn to accept responsibility. Taking responsibility simply means realizing something has to be done and doing it. It isn't always enjoyable to take responsibility. Sometimes being responsible is terribly inconvenient. It may be downright difficult. Quite often taking responsibility involves a lot of time and effort you'd rather spend doing something else.

Some responsibilities are forced upon you. Even though the end result may be good for you, the decision for you to accept the responsibility may be made by someone else, usually an adult.

For instance, you need to learn how to write well in order to succeed in today's complicated world. Your English teacher assigns a written project as homework. It is your responsibility to complete the assignment and do it well.

You know you need to be able to express yourself. You also realize you are responsible for doing your homework. It was your teacher, of course, who made the decision that you would do the homework. Even as you work on the assignment, you may resent the fact that you were forced to accept this responsibility.

Knowing that something is good or necessary does not always make it enjoyable. Realizing this is just part of taking responsibility.

Begin by listing five responsibilities that are forced upon you. After each responsibility, name the person, group, or circumstance that caused you to accept that responsibility. (A car that did not start, a sudden illness, or a bad storm are examples of circumstances.)

RESPONSIBILITY	**FORCE**
1. _____	_____
2. _____	_____
3. _____	_____
4. _____	_____
5. _____	_____

Choose one of the responsibilities you have just listed. Consider all the things that could happen if you fail or refuse to accept this particular responsibility. If you can think of positive results, be sure to include them. Most likely, most of the things that can happen will be negative, such as getting in hot water for failing to clean your room. Not getting the brakes fixed on your bike could result in death.

Responsibility: _____

Potential results if I don't accept this responsibility:

_____

_____

_____

_____

There may be reasons you feel you can not or should not accept certain responsibilities. Pick another one of the responsibilities you have listed above. Give the reasons you shouldn't have to do what you've been asked to do.

Responsibility: _____

Reasons I'm justified in not accepting this responsibility:

_____

_____

_____

_____

When you don't accept responsibility, someone has to take up the slack. Let's assume you've presented a good case for not accepting the responsibility you listed on the previous page. If you don't do it, who will?

_____

_____

_____

_____

Let's take a final look at the five responsibilities thrust upon you. Choose one of the remaining three. Tell why you are better suited to taking this responsibility than anyone else.

Responsibility: _____

Why I'm best able to handle this responsibility: _____

_____

_____

_____

_____

_____

_____

Taking Responsibility Is a Sign of Maturity

Babies and infants can't accept responsibility. Young children can be held responsible for some things but not for others. As the years pass, more and greater responsibilities are possible. Once a person is an adult, he or she must be able to accept personal responsibilities, and must also take on the responsibilities that go with doing a job, being a husband or wife, or raising a family.

The ability and willingness to accept responsibility go with growing up. Not everyone who is adult in body is truly an adult. Those who fail to accept responsibility or are unable to follow through on the responsibilities they do accept never really grow up. They are simply mature in years. They are not true adults.

We begin learning about responsibility when adults assign us to do certain things. Though it may not seem so at the time, these assignments are a sign of trust.

As we mature, we begin to take on responsibilities of our own. This is a positive indication that we are growing up.

Think of five responsibilities you have recently accepted because you chose to do so. Perhaps you didn't want to do what you did, but you went ahead and took the responsibility because it was necessary.

List these five responsibilities:

1. _____
2. _____
3. _____
4. _____
5. _____

What good things came as a result of your accepting responsibility? Choose one of the five responsibilities on your list and write down all the positive results.

Responsibility I accepted: _____

_____

Positive things that happened as a result: _____

_____

_____

_____

_____

In the years ahead, you're going to be called upon to accept a multitude of responsibilities. You will choose some responsibilities for yourself. Others will be thrust upon you as a result of getting an education, holding a job, being married, or raising a family.

Look ahead one year from now. List five major responsibilities you will probably choose to accept or have to accept during the coming year.

1. _____

2. _____

3. _____

4. _____

5. _____

Don't Shoot Yourself in the Foot

"Shooting yourself in the foot" doesn't mean you actually pulled the trigger and blew a hole in your foot. People shoot themselves in the foot when they do or say things that cause them problems. This is also known as *self-sabotage*.

Self-sabotage can happen even if we start out with the best intentions. Something interferes before we accomplish what we planned to do.

Self-sabotage is tricky. Often, the things that get in the way of our doing what we set out to do seem to be perfectly reasonable choices. For instance, "I was going to do my homework right after dinner but my sister needed help practicing her lines for the play."

Even after we've shot ourselves in our foot, it is often difficult to admit we've made a poor decision. For example, "I even had the vacuum cleaner out to start on my room when Wendy came over. She'd just broken up with Michael. By the time Wendy talked herself out it was too late to start cleaning my room."

Even the best intentions can get sidetracked when we let ourselves fall victim to self-sabotage.

On the next page are a "foot" and five "bullets."

Think back over the past few days or weeks. What are five good intentions you didn't accomplish? Use the numbered lines in the "foot."

In the five numbered "bullets," state briefly how you fell victim to self-sabotage and did something other than what you had planned.

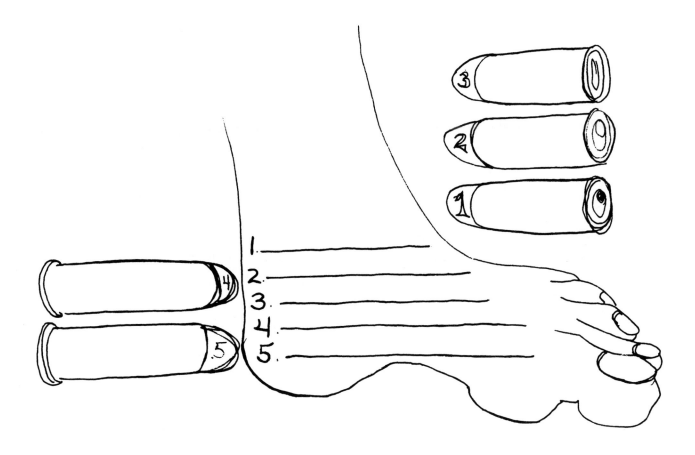

1. _____
2. _____
3. _____
4. _____
5. _____

Choose one of the above examples of self-sabotage. Look back at that incident and decide how you could have handled the situation so that you accomplished what you planned to do. Also, tell how you might have dealt with the item that caused you to avoid doing what you planned.

_____

_____

_____

_____

_____

_____

The Maker of Perfect Laws

At one time or another you've said or heard someone say, "There ought to be a law!" This means there is a problem that needs to be solved. Having a law is one way of attempting to solve a problem.

Unfortunately the law books are full of laws that often fail to solve the problems they were intended to solve. This is because laws are seldom perfect. A second problem comes when good laws are not obeyed or enforced.

Suppose you had the power to pass one law. This law would deal with your own life. It might include the lives of others but would center on your life and how you manage your life. Naturally, since you're dealing with your own life you want this to be a perfect law.

In the legal volume below write the perfect law you would enact.

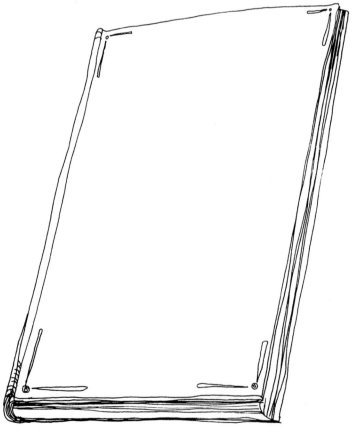

Explain briefly how this law would help you without hurting others.

_____

_____

_____

_____

_____

How would this perfect law be enforced?

_____

_____

_____

_____

_____

A License to Print Money

How many times have you wished you could just crank up the old copier and print a batch of money? Let's assume for a few minutes that you somehow were given permission to print all the money you wanted. In short, you had *a license to print money.*

Don't worry about deciding how much money you'd print. When you run out, you can just print more.

In the bill on the next page, list the five most important things you would do with the endless supply of money you have permission to print.

$

1. _____

_____

2. _____

_____

3. _____

_____

4. _____

_____

5. _____

_____

$

How would the five uses of money you've just listed change the way in which you live? Don't worry about how it might change the lives of others. Just consider what this would do for you and how it would alter the way you manage your life.

_____

_____

_____

_____

_____

_____

_____

No doubt you've heard the saying, "Money can't buy happiness." You've probably also heard the reply, "That's true, but I'd rather be rich and unhappy than poor and unhappy."

There are things money can't buy. Even with your wonderful license to print money, you can't have everything. What are three things you could not buy or accomplish no matter how much money was available to you?

1. _____

_____

2. _____

_____

3. _____

_____

Look back over the five things you would do with unlimited money. Check the three things money can't buy. Write five adjectives or short statements that describe the sort of person you are, based upon what you've written about money and its uses. For example: "Generous," or "I care about others."

1. _____

_____

2. _____

_____

3. _____

_____

4. _____

_____

5. _____

_____

Don't Let Stress Get You Down

People talk about stress daily. The terms *stressful* and *stressed out* are a part of our vocabulary. Stress is the cause of a number of problems. Many people also blame stress when they are unable to manage their lives.

We hear about stress, but what exactly is it? Stress is pressure or strain. It comes from a variety of sources that cause us to feel tense and ill at ease.

Most stress is a result of pressures coming from the outside world. Many of these we can't control. For example, getting big homework assignments in five classes on the same day can cause a lot of stress. So can crossing a dangerously busy street that has no stop lights. In both cases we have to deal with pressures over which we have no control. Both examples cause tenseness.

Stress also results from anticipating what may occur—whether it does or not. If you are afraid you'll be assigned a ton of homework on the night you want to go to the movies, you can become tense and stressed. Worrying if your parents are going to have another argument can be as stressful as actually hearing them yell at each other again.

To bring stress closer to home, look at the list of potentially stressful things on the next page. Some things may be stressful to children when they are young but not when they grow older.

Begin by placing a "Y" in the space to the left of each item if it is something likely to cause stress in young children. If an item is likely to cause stress in students your age, place a "T" in the space to stand for today. Items that you feel could cause stress in both students your age and in young children should be marked "YT."

_____ Fear of big dog   _____   _____ Getting lost   _____

_____ Breaking something _____   _____ An angry parent   _____

_____ First day of school _____   _____ Meeting strangers _____

_____ Daily chores   _____   _____ School work   _____

_____ Uncertainty   _____   _____ Asked to a dance   _____

_____ Learning to drive _____   _____ Not being chosen   _____

Go back over the list and decide which stressful items have caused you stress and how often. If an item *often* caused you stress, mark it with an "O" in the space to the right of that stress-maker. Items that seldom bother you should be marked "S." Those that never cause you stress may be marked with an "N" in the space to the right of the item.

By now you've thought of a number of things that can and do cause stress in your life at the present. Having a new brother or sister can be a joy but is also stressful. When a stepfather or stepmother becomes part of your life, it can be great but is still stressful to both of you. Going out for a team creates stress. So does making new friends or losing old friends. The pressure other students put on you can be very stressful.

List ten items or events in your life right now that cause stress.

1. _____

2. _____

3. _____

4. _____

5. _____

6. _____

7. _____

8. _____

9. _____

10. _____

Managing Stress

As you've already discovered, stress is a part of life. It can't be avoided. How you manage stress helps determine how happy and productive you are.

If you allow stress to build up inside you, the tensions it creates can hurt you. Both physical and mental health can be harmed by too much stress. A person who is really stressed is not a happy person.

Since there is no way we can avoid stress in life, the thing we must do is learn how to deal with stress. The strange thing is that some stress is actually good for us. It keeps us alert and helps us avoid getting into a rut.

Let's see how it is possible to deal with moderate stress and even make it work for us.

A big test is set for Monday. It's now Friday evening. You know you haven't prepared enough for the test. You are also aware that this test counts one-third of your term's grade. Blow this test and you've just flushed your grade for the term. This is sure to make you feel stressed.

You can spend the entire weekend worrying about the test so you're stressed all weekend. You can pretend to forget about the worry and then have a major bout with stress Sunday night at nine o'clock when you try to cram for the Monday test.

Or, you can let stress work for you to encourage you to study a little Friday evening, more Saturday, and a lot Sunday. In this case, you'll probably do well on the test. You will be saving your grade *and* your mental health at the same time.

Letting the stress caused by the test encourage you to set up a good study plan can not only reduce the stress, it can actually help you. This is one way to manage stress.

By now you have already thought of instances in which a stressful situation could encourage you to take action that helps you. Describe three moderately stressful situations in which the stress can help you by starting you off in the right direction.

In the spaces at the right of each stressful description, tell about the negative things that may occur if you don't handle the stress properly. Then describe how to turn this bit of stress into something positive.

NEGATIVE RESULTS

1. _____   _____

_____   _____

_____   **POSITIVE OUTCOMES**

_____   _____

_____

NEGATIVE RESULTS

2. _____   _____

   _____   _____

   _____   **POSITIVE OUTCOMES**

   _____   _____

                              _____

                              NEGATIVE RESULTS

3. _____   _____

   _____   _____

   _____   **POSITIVE OUTCOMES**

   _____   _____

                              _____

How to Keep Stress from Getting You Down

We can't avoid stress but we can deal with it. Now's the time to begin to devise some personal plans to help you cope with the stresses that are a normal part of growing up.

A good first step is to set realistic goals. Decide what needs to be done first and what can wait. At the same time, decide just how much you can accomplish.

For example, you want an A in English. Doing an extra credit book report will help. Doing two extra reports will really help! However, you have an essay that is due tomorrow and there's a punctuation test the following day.

Is it realistic to try to do the essay, review for the test, and read two books and write reports all tonight and tomorrow night? Of course not. But unless you set up a realistic set of goals you'll find stress getting to you.

This brings us to an important second step in avoiding stress. You need to organize your time.

In the above situation, it's a good idea to write the essay first since it's due tomorrow. Then, if you have time, begin reading the first book. Tomorrow night review for the punctuation test and continue reading. Plan ahead to see how soon you can reasonably finish the book and write the report. Jot a note on your calendar to remind you of your plan.

Look ahead and set a similar goal for reading and reporting on the second book. Make a note of that planned date as well.

Sounds simple, doesn't it? If it's so simple, why write down the dates? Because by writing the dates you're reducing stress. Once your planned dates are written, you don't have to keep remembering them. They are there for you to see.

Look at yourself at this moment. What realistic goals do you need to set for yourself? They may deal with school, with sports, with a project at home, or with any other important area in your life.

In the following space, briefly state what needs to be done and set a goal you can meet.

_____

_____

_____

_____

To reach the goal you have just set, you'll have to accomplish certain things. List the things you'll have to do to meet your goal.

_____

_____

_____

_____

Now decide on a logical order in which to accomplish these steps. List the steps in order at the left of the page. Beside each step give a date or time of day by which that step needs to be done.

1. _____   _____

2. _____   _____

3. _____   _____

4. _____   _____

5. _____   _____

An important step in keeping stress under control is learning to recognize what stressful things you can change or control and which are beyond your control.

You need to come to grips with the fact that trying to deal with things beyond your control wastes energy and time.

For instance, you can deal with the fact basketball practice is four nights each week by setting up a study schedule that takes into account that you're going to practice an hour and a half daily.

You *can't* change the terribly stressful fact that your mother and father have just been divorced. You can adjust to the change, but you can't make it go away.

Learning to recognize which stressful things you can control or change, and which ones you can't, helps reduce stress.

List ten things that are currently stressful to you. Write a "C" after each item you can *change* or *control.* Write an "N" for *no control* next to the items that are beyond your ability to change.

1. _____ ___   6. _____ ___

2. _____ ___   7. _____ ___

3. _____ ___   8. _____ ___

4. _____ ___   9. _____ ___

5. _____ ___   10. _____ ___

Now pick one item you decide you *can* change or control. Name that item here and tell briefly how you can go about changing or controlling it to help reduce stress in your life.

_____

_____

_____

_____

_____

You've probably heard the old saying, "All work and no play makes Jack a dull boy today." There's a lot of truth in this. One of the best ways to relieve stress is to take a break. Get some exercise. Go for a walk, take a bike ride, or jog around the park.

The change of pace helps get your mind off whatever it is you are doing. A little exercise lets you relax mentally while causing you to breathe deeper and use your muscles.

The amazing thing about taking an exercise break is not just that you return to the task feeling refreshed. Quite often you'll come back to work and discover you are able to deal with the problem or situation better than before you took your short break. Try it and see.

Getting Yourself Organized

Stress gets worse when things seem to be piling up more rapidly than you can cope with them. We've already mentioned that it helps to write down goals and dates to meet these goals.

It also helps to make a list of things that have to be done. Reducing the problem to writing helps. Having a list to refer to keeps your mind from trying to remember all those things that trouble you.

The time to begin getting organized is today. Don't wait until tomorrow.

Do you have daily chores and responsibilities? Do you tend to forget or put them off? If so, this causes stress.

A good way to deal with reducing this source of stress is to make a list of your chores and responsibilities. Name the item and list the time you should take care of it. Post this list on your note board, on the side of the refrigerator, or on your desk. The main thing is to put it where you see it often.

Set up a responsibility list now.

TASK   **WHEN TO DO**

_____   _____

_____   _____

_____   _____

_____   _____

If you add a task or have one you no longer need to do, just rewrite your list to reflect the change. Give this stress-reducer a try. It helps.

We can't mention enough times that writing things down helps. This is especially true of assignments. You can spend more time worrying over forgetting an assignment than you spend doing it.

Set up an assignment list. Name the class, tell what the assignment is, and note when it's due. Then, provide a column so you can check off the project when it's finished. Making that check mark not only indicates the assignment is complete, but it also gives you a lot of satisfaction.

Your assignment list can look like this:

SUBJECT	ASSIGNMENT	DESCRIPTION	DATE DUE	FINISHED

Fill in the above assignment list with current projects. When you run out of room, set up your own assignment list and keep it in your notebook. This list will really help reduce stress with multi-part projects and long-term assignments.

Finally, setting up a time chart helps you get yourself organized when you're really pressed for time. It can be quite simple and still do the job of organizing your time and lowering stress levels.

It isn't necessary to fill in the chart with your school day routine, unless you have to remember a special meeting or practice. Start your chart beginning with the end of the school day and ending with your bedtime.

List what needs doing and when. If you know how long it will take, give that information. For example, if you have cheerleading practice from 3:00 until 3:45 your chart might begin like this:

3:00   Cheerleading practice in gym   45 min.

If you know you're having dinner with your family at 6:30, that entry might look like this:

6:30   Dinner   30 min.

Fill in the things that have a set time such as household chores, practice, job, dinner, and the like. Leave space between them so you can insert items you can do at various times such as homework, do your nails, repair a flat on your bike, or call a friend to check on party plans for Friday night.

The important thing is to organize your time so that you don't waste time when you are busy. A good way to do this is to make a simple list stating when you're going to do what. This isn't something you have to do for every day of your life. It does help, however, when you have many things to do and not a lot of time.

Fill in the chart below for today, from the time school ends until you go to bed. You may discover you have more time than you realize.

TIME	*WHAT I'LL BE DOING*
_____	_____
_____	_____
_____	_____
_____	_____
_____	_____
_____	_____
_____	_____
_____	_____

TIME FLIES

If you find your weekends slipping away from you, set up a time chart for a weekend and see if it helps organize your time. It will help save you wasted time and will reduce stress because you know you won't forget something important. It's written down.

Go for Your Goal

Setting personal goals is an important part of organizing yourself. When you know where you want to go, it's much easier to get to your destination.

When you make a note of assignments due, you're *setting goals*. Your goal is to complete each assignment on time.

There are things in life other than assignments that become goals. Your goal may be as simple as remembering to get a haircut on Friday. It may be as complicated as learning all your lines in the class play in time for the first rehearsal.

Goals may be short–term—such as having your room cleaned before bedtime. They may be long–term to cover your desire to be first chair trumpet in time for the spring concert six months from now.

When setting goals, remember one of the ideas we've already discussed. Be realistic. Set goals you wish to meet but keep in mind you can only accomplish so much, no matter how much you wish to meet a goal. It is realistic to resolve to improve your ability on a musical instrument by increasing practice time. It's not realistic to resolve to become a starting offensive lineman on the school team when you weigh sixty pounds less than the average weight for the offensive line and have never made the team before.

Do a bit of goal-setting for the coming week. Consider six realistic goals that will benefit you once you've accomplished them. Write each goal between one set of goal posts.

When a goal is met, check off the pair of goal posts containing that goal. Figure your game score at the end of a week. Score six points for each goal you met. If you feel you came close to the goal but didn't quite make it, score three. For each goal you completely missed, subtract six points from your final score.

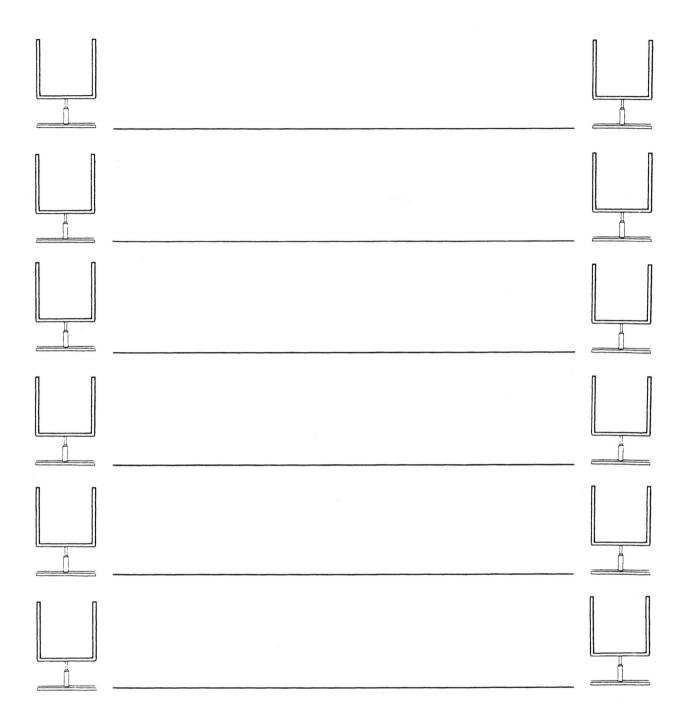

WEEK'S SCORE _____

Goals for the Month

Once you get in the habit of setting goals, it is natural for you to look ahead farther than a week at a time. Perhaps you've already set some life goals such as your choice of college, the profession you wish to work at, or places to which you wish to travel. Setting these goals and working toward them is part of what makes living worthwhile.

As part of your life both now and in the future, you'll be setting goals that can be achieved in less than ten or twenty years. You've already experienced setting weekly goals. Now how about looking forward for one month and setting some realistic goals you can achieve in that time.

What do you want to accomplish in the next month? In what areas do you wish to change or grow in the next thirty days? How far do you think you can advance in the next month?

Some people think of seven as a lucky number. With that in mind, how about setting seven realistic goals for the month ahead.

List the goals on the next page. It may be a good idea to have a copy of these seven goals posted in a place where you'll be reminded of the goals daily or several times daily. Think about having a copy on the desk in your room or perhaps taped to the inside of your locker door. It helps to be reminded of what you wish to accomplish or achieve. Though a month seems like a long time, it can quickly slip away.

1. _____
2. _____
3. _____
4. _____
5. _____
6. _____
7. _____

How many of the above goals did you meet during the month?

_____

It's Great to Be Successful

Success is what you make it. For some, being successful means making lots of money. For others, a successful person is one who lives a happy life and who has many good friends. Success is what makes you happy with yourself.

There have been countless rules for success over the years. Some common ones include the following:

Work hard.   **Honesty is the best policy.**

Learn to depend on yourself.   **Practice makes perfect.**

Save your money.

By now you have some personal rules for success that work for you. Think about the way you manage your life. What are your own rules for success?

You may have a number of rules for success or just a few. If you have more than ten, list the ten rules for personal success you feel are most important to you. If you have fewer than ten rules for your own success, use only the number of lines you need.

1. _____
2. _____

3. _____

4. _____

5. _____

6. _____

7. _____

8. _____

9. _____

10. _____

Here's How I Manage Myself

You have discovered quite a number of things about how you manage yourself. What works for you may not work in exactly the same way for someone else, but the general ideas you have found to be successful will help others.

Assume a friend has called to talk or is sitting across from you. Your friend is having trouble getting his or her life under control. Your friend's comments and questions are written out. After each of your friend's remarks is space for you to respond to what your friend just said.

Use what you've learned about managing yourself in this chapter to help you give your friend good advice.

Friend: "I'm all messed up. I just can't decide what to do. Life is so complicated! I just don't know how to make decisions."

You: _____

_____

_____

_____

_____

_____

Friend: "My folks are always nagging me. So are my teachers. They just don't understand. I wish they'd get off my back instead of talking about responsibility."

You: _____

_____

_____

_____

_____

_____

Friend: "I really do intend to get things done. But then something important always comes up."

You: _____

_____

_____

_____

_____

_____

Friend: "You can't believe how stressed-out I am! I just can't handle any more stress. Every time I turn around there's more pressure on me."

You: _____

_____

_____

_____

_____

_____

Friend: "That's fine for you to say because you're always so well organized. Me, I can never even find the time to do my homework."

You: _____

_____

_____

_____

_____

_____

Friend: "The thing is, I'm just living from day to day. I don't really know where I want to be tomorrow or next week."

You: _____

_____

_____

_____

_____

_____

Friend: "What you say makes sense. What makes you so successful?"

You: _____

_____

_____

_____

_____

_____

4

Others and Me

It is common for others to see you differently than you see yourself. You may think of yourself as calm and reasonable. A friend who has seen you upset might consider you easily excited and demanding. When you look in the mirror, you may see a person who works hard but often is the victim of circumstance. One of your teachers may think of you as a student with lots of potential who does not put enough energy into his or her

work and is quick to blame outside influences for failures.

For any of a variety of reasons parents, relatives, friends, and teachers may expect something of you that you can't or don't accomplish. Likewise, you may sometimes expect your relatives or friends to accomplish things that they just can't or don't do.

Quite often we see ourselves differently than others see us. At the same time, we view others in a totally different light than they view themselves.

Great Expectations

We do and say things because they are expected of us. We also act in ways we think others expect us to act. Generally we have a pretty good idea of what others expect. At times we're way off-base in the way we think others view us.

Children and youth generally understand, or think they understand, their parents' feelings toward them. Part of these feelings involve what our parents expect of us. What are the five most important things your parents expect of you?

1. _____

2. _____

3. _____

4. _____

5. _____

Now let's turn this around for a moment. What are the five most important things you expect from your parents?

1. _____

2. _____

3. _____

4. _____

5. _____

The expectations of friends often carry as much weight, or even more, than do those of parents and family. What are the three major things your best friend expects of you?

1. _____

2. _____

3. _____

Since friendship involves closeness, it is only natural to expect certain things from your friends. Name the three most important things you expect from your best friend as a part of your friendship.

1. _____

2. _____

3. _____

It's not uncommon to discover we are trying to live up to expectations we think others have of us, but that they really don't. Ask your parents to list the three expectations they hold for you. List them here.

1. _____

2. _____

3. _____

How nearly correct were you when it came to knowing what your parents expect of you? Did your list include all three of the expectations your parents listed?

Getting Along with Others

The world can be a lonely place when we don't get along well with the people around us. Take a few minutes to complete this survey. It won't tell you everything about yourself and others, but it will give you something to consider regarding how you relate to other people.

Check the space under the response which *most nearly* describes how you react to each statement.

	YES	NO	AT TIMES
1. I get along well with most people.	___	___	___
2. I like most people I know.	___	___	___
3. Most people seem to like me.	___	___	___
4. I worry about what others think of me.	___	___	___
5. When I listen to others I'm usually waiting for them to stop so I can talk.	___	___	___
6. It's difficult for me to change my ideas and plans instead of having my own way.	___	___	___
7. Sometimes I goof off so I can be the center of attention.	___	___	___
8. I make up excuses rather than face the true facts.	___	___	___
9. I often pout or feel sorry for myself when I don't have what I'd like to have.	___	___	___

	YES	NO	AT TIMES
10. I tend to think of myself first when planning for the future.	____	____	____
11. I do my share.	____	____	____
12. Meeting strangers and making new friends comes easily.	____	____	____
13. I'm lonely and need more friends.	____	____	____
14. People don't understand me.	____	____	____
15. I am a good sport even when I'm not happy with the outcome.	____	____	____

When you look back at the way you responded to some of these statements, you may get the feeling you aren't the sort of person you'd like to be. Don't let that feeling get you down if it occurs. You aren't perfect even though you'd like to be. But you aren't a bad person either.

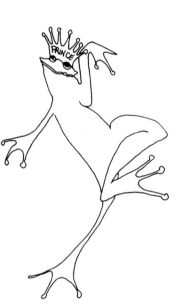

If you really want to see how others look at you, ask someone you know and trust to react to this set of statements. Simply read the sentences to that person. Mark his or her responses on this sheet with a different colored pen or pencil.

Remember that you asked this person for his or her opinions. Don't get bent out of shape if your trusted friend comes up with answers you may not expect. At the same time don't be surprised if your friend sees you in a better light than you see yourself.

What About the Generation Gap?

There is nothing new about the generation gap. Ever since parents had children and then became grandparents, we've had a difference of views and opinions between the generations.

This way of looking at things, depending upon differences in age and experience, may cause problems for those on both sides of the gap. Older people tend to say things such as, "When I was your age...." People your age are just as likely to remark, "You don't understand. Things are different now."

Let's take a look at some areas in which the generation gap can result in some major differences in opinions and expectations. First, give your views about each area in a few words. Then briefly give the views of your parents and other members of your parents' generation. (Consider teachers as part of that generation even if they are older or younger than your parents.)

	My View	*Older Generation's View*
Homework	_____	_____
	_____	_____
	_____	_____
Chores	_____	_____
	_____	_____
	_____	_____

	MY VIEW	*OLDER GENERATION'S VIEW*

Brothers and sisters _____   _____

_____   _____

_____   _____

My friends _____   _____

_____   _____

_____   _____

TV _____   _____

_____   _____

_____   _____

Bedtime _____   _____

_____   _____

_____   _____

The mall _____   _____

_____   _____

_____   _____

Dates and going steady _____   _____

_____   _____

_____   _____

Now how about making a diagram of the generation gap you've just covered. Think of the edges of the paper as a major gap in the way you and your parents and other adults view things. Consider the center of the paper as an area in which you and adults have almost the same feelings.

If you and your parents are fairly far apart in your thinking draw two vertical lines like those below.

If you are close to your parents, the lines would be closer:

Now connect the vertical lines so they look like this for the two sets of generation gap lines you've done.

Consider each set of comments you've made. Draw your generation gap lines beside (or maybe through) the words in the center of the page to show how close or how distant your thinking is from that of your parents. Then connect the lines as in the illustration above. When this is done, you'll have a diagram of your own generation gap.

Homework

Chores

Brothers and sisters

My friends

TV

Bedtime

The mall

Dates and going steady

What It Means to Be a Member of a Family

You didn't have any choice as to which family you joined. You were born part of a family. Being a member of a family is more than just being born into that family. How you feel and act and how other family members feel and act determines whether yours is a happy, understanding family, or one in which members don't work together for the good of all.

At times you may feel your parents or other family members are being unfair in the way they treat you. This is a normal feeling and not all that uncommon. Usually, if you can look at an event through the eyes of an outsider—or better yet through the eyes of another family member—you might realize the reaction you thought was unfair makes perfect sense to others in the family.

Being part of a family involves cooperation and understanding. It means accepting differences in the feelings of other family members. Being a family member requires a willingness to meet other members halfway to create a pleasant family environment.

You've considered the generation gap. Now try to put yourself in your parents' shoes for a few minutes. How would you react in the following situations? Keep in mind you want your children to be happy and to love you. Yet you are responsible for guiding them and helping to keep them safe.

1. Your fourteen-year-old son or daughter promised to be home by eleven from a Coke and pizza party. He or she is just now arriving home. It is ten past midnight. This is the third weekend in a row your child has promised to be home by a certain time and has arrived an hour or so later.

What are you feelings toward your child? (worried, angry, depressed)

_____

Why do you feel as you do?

_____

_____

As a parent, what would you do and say about this situation?

_____

_____

_____

_____

_____

2. When your thirteen-year-old daughter started dating a seventeen-year-old high school junior, you suggested she date fellows closer to her own age. After several tearful discussions she agreed. You believed her. This evening, by accident, you saw your daughter at the mall. She was holding hands with the seventeen-year-old. Seconds after, you saw the two of them embrace and kiss.

How do you feel toward your daughter? (sad, shocked, disgusted)

_____

_____

_____

_____

_____

_____

What makes you feel this way? _____

_____

_____

_____

How will you react as her parent? What will you say? When will you say it? _____

_____

_____

_____

_____

3. When your son started smoking at the age of twelve, you realized it was because he wanted to belong. You discussed health problems associated with smoking and he quit on his own. Now he's fourteen and you know your son is drinking when he goes out with the guys. He smells like a keg of beer tonight and his speech is slurred. What are your feelings toward your son? (displeased, shocked, sad)

_____

_____

_____

Why do you have these specific feelings?

_____

_____

_____

_____

What are you going to do and say at this point?

_____

_____

_____

By now you've probably already recalled a number of times you and your parents have discussed or even argued over things you've done or not done. No doubt part of the misunderstandings came as a result of their high expectations for you. Your need for independence enters in as well.

Devise three rules you can follow that will help you respect the rights and wishes of the rest of your family but will still allow you to make decisions on your own. In short, what three rules of life and conduct can you come up with to help make you a good family member without taking away any of your personal rights?

1. _____

2. _____

3. _____

Not Me!

It is sometimes difficult to accept responsibility for things that go wrong. There is a tendency in many of us to look for an excuse to take the blame from our shoulders. It is normal to try to blame someone else for our own failures. This is because we often feel we've diminished ourselves in the eyes of others when we make mistakes or fail.

Friends and family can accept mistakes and failures more easily than they can accept constant excuses and blaming of others. This is something very young children often find difficult to understand.

Most of us learn to admit our errors and try to remedy our mistakes. A few people spend their entire lives blaming "them" or "society" or "the government" for their failures. These people tend to lead unhappy lives.

Look back on your early childhood. What was an early disaster you caused, such as breaking your mother's best vase or losing some of your father's tools? Describe that early disaster.

_____

_____

Did you admit you were at fault or did you try to shift the

blame? _____

_____

_____

How did your family react? _____

_____

_____

_____

At some time in recent months or years you've been tempted to say "Not me," or "I didn't do it," when you were entirely, or at least partially, to blame for something that went wrong or was left undone.

Why were you unwilling or unable to admit you were at fault?

_____

_____

Were you eventually found out, or did you finally take responsibility for what went wrong? _____

_____

_____

What happened to you as a result of taking responsibility, if you did? _____

_____

_____

If you escaped detection and never admitted being at fault, what did you gain and what did you lose by your actions?

_____

_____

_____

_____

Let's conclude this section by looking at the blame from another angle. Have you been blamed for something you did not do? Most of us have, so you don't have to feel as though you're alone.

How did you happen to get wrongfully blamed? Were you a victim of circumstance or did someone set you up to take their blame?

_____

_____

_____

_____

What was the outcome of this incident? Did you convince others of your innocence?

_____

_____

_____

Take a close look at yourself. Why are you able to accept the consequences of your own mistakes or why not? How does this ability or lack of ability have an effect on the way you get along with others?

_____

_____

_____

Good Friends Are Worth Keeping

You probably know hundreds of people by name. You recognize hundreds more when you see them. If asked, you may say you have dozens or even hundreds of friends. But how many *good* friends do you have?

Most people consider themselves lucky to have a handful of truly good friends. We are acquainted with many, but most of our friends are actually people we meet and know who aren't extremely close to us.

What do you look for in choosing friends? What qualities make another person likely to become your friend?

_____

_____

_____

_____

What things about you make you a good friend to others?

_____

_____

_____

_____

We aren't perfect. You are no exception. Can you identify negative qualities you have that might make others hesitate about considering you a good friend?

_____

_____

_____

Even best friends sometimes have misunderstandings. What once led to an argument or misunderstanding between you and someone you considered a good or even best friend?

_____

_____

Why did you feel you were right and your friend was wrong?

_____

_____

What may have caused your friend to feel you were wrong?

_____

_____

How did the two of your resolve your differences?

_____

_____

If you didn't solve the problem, what kept you from doing so?

_____

_____

_____

If you had to give the three most important benefits of close friendship, what would they be?

1. _____

2. _____

3. _____

What Do They Say When I'm Not Around?

It's human nature to talk about those we know. We tell stories about one another, we pay compliments, we retell incidents, and sometimes we make negative statements. Even best friends may make negative comments about each other when talking to others.

Have you ever stopped to wonder what people say about you when you're not around? Of course you have. We all have moments in which we pause and ask ourselves how others really feel about us. You are a rare individual if you haven't ever wondered about this.

Sometimes we are pleased when a friend says, "Jennifer said the nicest thing about you." Other times it hurts when we're told, "Mike isn't the good friend you think he is. You should hear what he's been saying about you."

Take a few minutes to consider both the nicest and the worst things others might truthfully say about you. Try to look at yourself from their point of view.

What good thing would you expect your best female friend to say about you when talking to others?

_____

_____

_____

What's the most negative thing she might say?

_____

_____

_____

What do you think would be the nicest thing for your best male friend to tell others when talking about you?

_____

_____

_____

What's the worst thing he might tell others?

_____

_____

_____

What's the most positive statement a family member might make to someone outside your family?

_____

_____

_____

What negative thing might that same relative say?

_____

_____

_____

If all your teachers had to agree on one really great thing to say about you, what would it be?

_____

_____

_____

What's the worst thing those same teachers could agree to say about you?

_____

_____

_____

But They're My Friends!

Going along with the gang or doing what your friends expect of you is known as *peer pressure.* Peers are others near your own age. What other students expect of you is extremely important.

How many times have you done something with others you wouldn't have done on your own? How often have you wanted to have a certain brand of clothing or a specific item because your friends had the same thing? Even though no one said you needed that brand or that item, you felt you did. This is a form of peer pressure.

We want to belong, to be accepted, to be part of the group. These desires are what make peer pressure such a strong influence. It's no fun to feel left out and different.

Neither is it a good idea to make your decisions because of peer pressure. You have certain values. Living up to those values often means going against peer pressure.

Coming right out and challenging your peers is no fun. Sometimes you have to decide whether your values or those of your peers are going to control your decisions.

Just Say No sounds simple. It sounds too simple to solve much of anything, but it is the basis for keeping peer pressure from taking away your freedom of choice.

The trick is to say "no" firmly but in a manner that doesn't sound like you're making excuses. Consider how to say "no" in the following situations.

The gang is going for pizza but afterwards wants to chug a couple of six-packs.

Marilyn's folks are out of town and she's having a party. Last time the same kids partied, they trashed a home.

Bud's folks drove his father's car to dinner. Bud has the keys to his mother's car and is going out for a spin. Bud's fourteen.

A big thing to stay away from when dealing with peer pressure is making excuses. When you make an excuse it is almost always an invitation for someone to come up with a reason why your excuse is no good.

How do you best respond to the following situations without making an excuse which can be shot down?

"Have a cigarette. Everyone in our group smokes."

_____

_____

_____

"You're uptight. Pop a couple of these and you'll be so mellow you'll think you're floating."

_____

_____

_____

"There's nothing to it. You get the clerk's attention and I'll slip out the door with the stuff in this K-Mart bag."

_____

_____

_____

Sometimes it helps take the pressure off if you postpone making a decision for a while. The down side is that you must eventually come to a decision. On the plus side you have time to consider your options.

What might you say in order to delay the decisions in the following situations? Remember to avoid excuses others can get around.

You've been asked to donate time to the neighborhood center. You really don't want to commit yourself to this task.

_____

_____

_____

Three friends want you to go out for track, but you want to work on your tennis game this spring.

_____

_____

_____

Some of the most popular kids in school are collecting money for a party next Saturday afternoon down at the lake. You want no part of it.

_____

_____

_____

People have different feelings about peer pressure. Sum up your feelings in a short statement. Keep in mind not all peer pressure is bad.

_____

_____

_____

What Are My Values?

We begin acquiring values at an early age. Children tend to accept many of the same values as their parents. When school begins, some of the values held by teachers are normally accepted by their students. The values of a person's peers and close friends often become that person's own values.

Your own values depend upon the values of those around you and how you feel about these people and their values. Your personal values help you to decide how you live your life.

When your values don't agree with those of others, conflict may result. Friends may disagree, groups may reject an individual, and society can come down hard on one whose values are vastly different.

In each of the following situations, decide whether your values will let you take part or not. List the values that will help you make your decision.

Your social studies teacher gave the same test last year. Stan's sister kept a copy. He is willing to share with you. The test is tomorrow. Your mother will come down hard if you don't do well. You've got play practice tonight so study time is limited.

_____

_____

_____

Donna doesn't have a lot of spending money. You just found out that Donna shoplifts clothing and makeup she can't afford to buy. She's a good friend. Donna has offered to pick up an item you want but can't afford.

_____

_____

_____

You knew Larry and his father didn't get along. Today Larry is moving poorly and has bruises on his face. He admits to you his father beat him up again. You want to report it. Larry says that will just make things worse for him and his younger brother. You ask yourself what happens if this is not reported.

_____

_____

_____

That's Not What I Meant

Simple statements and gestures can turn people off. You don't have to plan to hurt others in order for your words or expressions to give them pain. Once you say something that hurts, others are likely to remember it. Even if you didn't intend harm, what you said may be held against you.

Someone makes a suggestion you don't agree with. Without thinking you say, "That's a really stupid idea!" Perhaps it wasn't the greatest idea in the world. But by calling it stupid you've hurt the feelings of the person who made the suggestion. You could have caused less hurt feeling by saying, "Can you explain that? I don't see how it's going to work."

How about the time you offered an idea and someone rolled her eyes to show she felt your idea was silly or childish. How did you feel toward her?

Just a little consideration for the feelings of others goes a long way. This is certainly true when it comes to thoughtless remarks and those little gestures that put others down.

Think of a thoughtless remark you've made in the past that may have hurt someone's feelings. What did you say?

_____

_____

_____

How might you have said this to avoid hurt feelings?

_____

_____

_____

You've been hurt by being on the receiving end of blunt or cruel statements. What has been said to you that left you feeling put down and hurt?

_____

_____

_____

_____

How did that state-
ment leave you feeling
toward the person who
made it?

_____

_____

_____

_____

_____

How did you feel
about yourself?

_____

_____

_____

What are three gestures people make that let others know they
are putting someone down without saying a word?

1. _____

2. _____

3. _____

Many of us have our own favorite gesture, look, or body move-
ment that clues others in when we're putting someone down. After
using this a number of times, it sometimes becomes so automatic
we don't think about it. What is your personal favorite in this area?

_____

_____

_____

Pretend you're on the receiving end of the move you just described. How might it make you feel?

_____

_____

_____

_____

I Haven't Been That Angry in a Long Time!

Anger is a normal reaction to a number of things that happen to us. Feeling angry toward someone or something is nothing to be ashamed of. What is important is how you handle your anger so it does not cause you major problems.

When you let your anger take control, you end up in conflict with others. This may result in an exchange of words or even in physical violence. When this happens, you've allowed your anger to replace logic.

Let's look at several ways to handle anger. Then you can decide which is the best way to deal with this normal but potentially destructive emotion.

First, you can keep your feelings of anger bottled up inside you. Instead of saying anything or striking out, you can keep others from realizing just how angry you are.

What is likely to result if you try to keep all your feelings of anger hidden inside you?

_____

_____

_____

A second method of dealing with anger is to direct that anger toward people or things not even involved. For example, you can snap at your mother because you and a friend have had an argument, or you can kick the wastepaper basket for the same reason.

What can be good and what's bad about venting your anger on someone or something not responsible for the problem?

_____

_____

_____

_____

There's a third way to deal with your anger. You can yell, scream, and perhaps start swinging. Even though this tends to make things worse, it is a fairly common method of trying to cope with the strong emotion of anger, especially among young children and the emotionally immature.

What are the obvious negative results of this means of dealing with your anger?

_____

_____

_____

Is there a positive side of this way to handle anger?

_____

_____

_____

There is also a fourth method many people use to control anger. They simply stay away from people and situations they know from experience will make them angry.

There are some drawbacks to this means of avoiding anger. What are they?

_____

_____

_____

You've considered a number of ways to handle your anger. None of them are perfect. Some are really poor.

How would you like others to deal with the situation when they have become angry at you? Describe the way you'd like others to react when they have a problem with you that has made them angry.

_____

_____

_____

Take a quick look at your own reactions when you're angry. Are there any things you do that are different from the way you'd like others to act when they are angry?

_____

_____

_____

_____

The Way I Feel

There are many words in your vocabulary to express the way you feel—words such as happy, sad, elated, upset, downcast, and excited, for example.

Make a list of words that describe feelings. "Happy" can start the positive list and "sad" can begin your negative list.

POSITIVE

_____   _____

_____   _____

_____   _____

_____   _____

_____   _____

_____   _____

_____   _____

               _____

NEGATIVE

_____   _____

_____   _____

_____   _____

_____   _____

_____   _____

_____   _____

               _____

These words are among those you use to describe your feelings to others. Did you ever stop to think that the words you use about your feelings have a lot to do with the way other people think of you and react to you?

Choose any three positive feeling words from your list on the previous page. Write them here.

_____

Now pretend you've just used those three words in a conversation with a friend. Describe how your friend is likely to feel about you as a result of the words you've just used.

_____

_____

_____

Now select three negative words from your list and write them here.

_____

Assume you've just used those negative words as you talk to your friend. How does your friend probably feel about you now?

_____

_____

_____

Body Language

The way we move says a lot to others about us. Did you ever stop to consider what your body language says to others? Probably not. But when you think for a few seconds, you'll quickly realize how much you learn about others from watching the way they move and hold their bodies.

For example, there goes a man with his eyes partially closed. He walks slowly and carefully and looks straight ahead. Automatically you think to yourself, "Poor fellow has a terrible headache."

When we see a person suddenly break into a big smile and punch a fist into the air, we know instantly something really good has just happened.

We tell others a great deal about our feelings and attitudes from our movements and the gestures we make. The way we hold our head and the manner in which we glance about give others a clue to how we feel and even what we are thinking.

A ducked head and darting glances give one impression, while a steady stride and freely swinging hands send an entirely different message.

Describe how your body moves and looks when you feel the following emotions. Don't forget such body parts as hands, jaw, lips, and eyes in your descriptions.

You just checked your quarter's report card and it is wonderful.

_____

_____

_____

You're so angry you feel as though you could explode.

_____

_____

_____

It's your first day in a new school. You don't know anyone and can't find your second period classroom.

_____

_____

_____

The great looking fellow or girl you want to meet has just walked into the room. You want to make a good impression.

_____

_____

_____

A grandparent you really love is in the hospital in intensive care.

_____

_____

_____

Body language tells others more than we realize. In the space below, sum up the various movements and postures that send out positive messages to others. Then, on the next page, list negative message senders.

POSITIVE BODY LANGUAGE

_____

_____

_____

_____

_____

_____

NEGATIVE BODY LANGUAGE

_____

_____

_____

_____

_____

_____

That's Not True!

Lies are an unfortunate part of life. Some of us use lies in an attempt to get out of trouble. Others lie in an effort to get even or to discredit another person. Sometimes we lie to try to appear more important or better skilled than we are when we want to impress someone.

We sometimes face the difficult task of needing to convince others that an untrue statement made about us is wrong. It's easy to disprove someone's statement that you have two thumbs on your right hand. You only need to hold out your right hand.

But how do you go about convincing your family you did not drink and use drugs at an overnight party if someone has told them otherwise? How do you prove to a teacher you did not get outside help on a take-home test? How do you make a friend believe you were not the one who spread a nasty rumor about him or her?

Someone has lied about you. As a result your mother is on your case and ready to ground you until you graduate from high school. What can you do or say to convince your mother you're telling the truth?

_____

_____

_____

Because of someone's vicious lie, your best friends are acting as though you have the plague. They won't talk with you, sit near you, or have anything to do with you. How do you prove the lie was untrue?

_____

_____

_____

Two police officers are at the door. You know you had nothing to do with any crime. You can also guess someone lied about you to take some heat off himself or herself. What do you say to convince the officers you were home alone, studying, at the time of the crime?

_____

_____

_____

What do you feel are your three best defenses against becoming the victim of lies told by others?

1. _____

2. _____

3. _____

How can you defend yourself against lies others may tell about you? Sometimes you can't. The sad fact is that people who are jealous, angry, or hurt sometimes lie about others in an effort to deprive them of respect, love, rewards, or success.

The best defense you have against becoming the victim of someone's falsehood is to be the very best person you can be. If you work hard at being a good person, your friends and all who know you will recognize untrue statements when they hear them. They will know you for the person you really are and will ignore lies or defend your reputation when they hear lies being told about you.

For this reason, it's a good idea to talk to friends when you become aware someone is spreading untrue rumors about you. Ignoring falsehoods may seem to be the best defense, but sometimes it can backfire. Some people will think you're afraid to face what's being said if you pretend to ignore rumors and lies.

Let your friends know you're aware of what's being said. Try not to appear angry. Point out why the lie or rumor can't be true. If someone can identify the source of the lies, you can often figure out why that person is angry, hurt, or jealous.

If you can remain calm, it may help to confront the rumor spreader. Just don't let it turn into a shouting match, or worse.

Even though you won't like the suggestion, there are times when it helps to talk things over with an adult such as your teacher or counselor. No one likes to run to authority figures when the going gets rough. There are times, however, when an adult in authority can help solve a problem. That's why nations sit down with mediators at peace talks.

Is Honesty Always Best?

Being honest simply means telling the truth. That's easy to understand. We're taught to tell the truth from early childhood. Most of us feel being honest with ourselves is a basic value in our lives.

Are there times when complete honesty is not always the best policy? Read each question and decide which answer best fits the situation.

1. Should you tell your friend you really don't like his or her new clothing when you're asked?

   ___ *ALWAYS*   ___ *USUALLY*   ___ *NEVER*

2. Is it dishonest if you don't tell your parents everything you do when you're out with your friends?

   ___ *ALWAYS*   ___ *USUALLY*   ___ *NEVER*

3. Are you being dishonest if you take the blame for someone else?

   ___ *ALWAYS*   ___ *USUALLY*   ___ *NEVER*

4. You know someone is cheating on a test. Are you being dishonest if you don't tell the teacher?

   ___ *ALWAYS*   ___ *USUALLY*   ___ *NEVER*

5. You pretend to agree with the gang to avoid trouble. Does this make you dishonest?

   ___ *ALWAYS*   ___ *USUALLY*   ___ *NEVER*

6. Is it dishonest to give an answer to a personal question that does not completely answer the question?

   ___ *ALWAYS*   ___ *USUALLY*   ___ *NEVER*

7. You have to lie to keep a surprise secret. Are you dishonest?

   ___ *ALWAYS*   ___ *USUALLY*   ___ *NEVER*

8. A friend asks what someone has said about him or her. You don't tell the truth because what was said was hurtful. Are you being dishonest?

   ___ *ALWAYS*   ___ *USUALLY*   ___ *NEVER*

Part of getting along with others involves living and acting in such a way that you don't hurt them. At the same time, you have to avoid doing or saying something that will cause others to think badly of you.

Sum up your own personal thoughts on honesty and dishonesty. Give the three most important ones here.

1. _____

_____

_____

2. _____

_____

_____

3. _____

_____

_____

That's Good News!

We all like to receive good news. Good news can really brighten a day.

Suppose you had the chance to decide on what good news you'd receive. Give some thought to what sort of good news you'd like to receive in each of the following instances. Then write your choice of good news in each case.

You've just gotten a paper back from a teacher. The teacher has written some good news in the upper corner of the page. Write a message that you would feel was really great news.

TEST **Period 2**
1. Find the gravitational force exerted by one weight.

A friend has just passed you a note between classes. Fill in the note below wth the best news that note might contain.

To You **From Me**

Someone called while you were studying at the library after school. A member of your family left you a message stuck to the side of the refrigerator. Write a good news message you'd like to receive when you got home.

A Call Came While You Were Out. **The Message Was:**

You're Invited

Invitations are fun. Parties and special events are exciting. If you had your choice, who would invite you to a party or social occasion? Where would this take place? What sort of party or celebration would it be?

Complete this invitation to you. Fill in all the necessary information for a party event to which you'd really like to be invited.

YOU ARE INVITED

Who is invited? _____

What's happening? _____

_____

What's the date? _____

What are the hours? _____

Where's the event? _____

What's the dress code? _____

Who's the host or hostess? _____

R.S.V.P. before Monday

The Power of Friends

How our friends feel and act toward us and what they say about us can go a long way toward making us happy or sad. Such is the power of friendship.

Complete each statement based on how you feel about what you and your friends should do for and feel toward each other.

1. A friend can make my day better by _____

_____

2. I become unhappy or hurt when a friend _____

_____

3. When choosing a friend, I want that person to be _____

_____

4. One of the best things a friend can do for me is _____

_____

5. The kindest thing a friend ever did for me was _____

_____

6. Sometimes my friends help me _____

_____

7. A real friend is one who _____

_____

A Special Bouquet

Flowers have long been a symbol of love and friendship. You're going to design a special bouquet to sum up what you've discovered about yourself and your relationship with others.

One flower in the bouquet is you. In that flower list the qualities and values which make you a special person.

The three other flowers in the bouquet stand for three people who are important in your life. A flower can represent a parent, a relative, a friend, or any other person who is important in your life. Give that person's name along the stem of his or her flower.

In each blossom list the things that make this person so special.

5

Everyone Isn't Like Me

There is no question but that you're different from everyone else. After all, you're you. Little differences make you a unique individual.

Because you're different from other people does not mean you're not like millions of others in many ways. Your differences don't keep you from having strong opinions about the way others should act and the kind of characteristics people need to have.

You can't change the fact that everyone isn't like you. You *can*, however, set standards that you feel others need in order to be people you wish to spend time with.

Characteristics a Perfect Father Should Have

Let's begin by having you decide on the characteristics a man would have who is a perfect father. Since no one is perfect, you may come up with a few characteristics not all fathers share.

Do keep one idea in mind. Just because a father falls short of total perfection does not mean he isn't a good father. Fatherhood is like many things in life. No matter how hard a person works at being a good father, there are always going to be a few things children might like to change.

In the space before each characteristic below, make a check mark if you feel this is a characteristic of a good father.

_____ handsome	_____ expects perfection
_____ kind	_____ never shows anger
_____ stern	_____ never fails
_____ harsh	_____ shows when he's pleased
_____ sometimes cries	
_____ honest	_____ loving
_____ takes care of you	_____ laughs a lot
	_____ works hard
_____ gentle	_____ brave
_____ willing to listen	_____ never wrong

Now add ten characteristics of a good father which are not given above.

_____	_____
_____	_____
_____	_____
_____	_____
_____	_____

Characteristics a Perfect Mother Should Have

Mothers, like fathers, are seldom perfect. Try as they may, mothers do things of which their children don't always approve. The fact that mothers aren't perfect doesn't keep them from being good mothers. It just goes along with the fact that they, like their children, are human beings.

Check those characteristics listed below which you feel should be displayed by women who are good mothers. Don't condemn your mother or any other mother who falls a bit short of being perfect.

—— forgiving   —— depends on others

—— thoughtful   —— does what she says

—— accepts mistakes   —— brave

—— beautiful   —— kind

—— expects obedience   —— strong willed

—— honest   —— understanding

—— hardworking   —— loving

—— fun to be with   —— takes care of you

—— demanding   —— lets you please her

—— listens well

List ten additional characteristics that haven't been mentioned on the previous page.

—————————————   —————————————

—————————————   —————————————

—————————————   —————————————

—————————————   —————————————

—————————————   —————————————

We *Always* Do It This Way

There are things in everyone's lives that they do simply because it is expected of them. When you asked, as a young child, why your family did some particular thing, you may have been told, "We've always done it that way," or "It's part of our family tradition."

There is nothing wrong with keeping family traditions. This is one way in which a family's past history lives on. Keeping old traditions helps the present generation remember those who lived before. It's a way of helping families have a sense of togetherness.

Are there family traditions that no longer seem to make sense to you? Would you rather try something different?

Every family has its own traditions as well as those it shares with countless other families. You may enjoy all of your family's traditions, or you may dislike a few.

Think about your family traditions. They might include having oyster soup on one certain night of the year, going to church on Christmas eve, visiting a relative at the same time each week, eating the same meal for Sunday dinner each week, and so on.

List ten things you do with your family because they are traditions. In the space after each tradition make an "x" if this is a tradition you enjoy and would like to continue.

1. _____ _____

2. _____ _____

3. _____ _____

4. _____ _____

5. _____ _____

6. _____ _____

7. _____ ____

8. _____ ____

9. _____ ____

10. _____ ____

Since you are not entirely like your parents and ancestors, there may be things you'd like to try that might become family traditions. Just because your family hasn't done them before doesn't mean you wouldn't enjoy them.

What are five family traditions you've read or heard about that you'd like to have your own family try?

1. _____

2. _____

3. _____

4. _____

5. _____

Families aren't the only groups who have traditions. Schools, communities, people with similar backgrounds, and even nations have traditions, too. Things such as the Fourth of July parade, the Friday pep rally, and Thanksgiving are traditions common to most of us.

What are five traditions outside your family that you think are great and you hope continue forever? After each tradition, tell what group holds that tradition (school, church, city, for example).

	TRADITION	*GROUP*
1.	_____	_____
2.	_____	_____
3.	_____	_____
4.	_____	_____
5.	_____	_____

Can you think of any things you'd like to see become traditions? Perhaps no one has ever suggested them. Maybe they were tried once and given up. For instance, giving school letters for good grades as well as for athletics might be a great tradition if your school would give it a try.

Give one thing you'd like to see become a tradition for each of the groups below.

School _____

Community _____

Nation _____

Other _____

How Do I Compare?

We constantly compare ourselves with others. It's human nature to do so.

It's only when we let these comparisons get out of hand that they can cause problems. If we compare ourselves with others and constantly feel we're lacking in every area, it may cause depression. On the other hand, those who always feel they are superior to others in every way can become the boasting sort of people others can't stand.

Comparing yourself with others is a good way to help you understand how you are alike and how you differ from other people. It's also a good way to help realize that though you're superior in some areas, you may be average or ordinary in others. You'll also find that even if you feel less capable than other people, you rate high in other areas.

If you compare yourself with others, you can see that while you're not like everyone else, you are still very much like others.

A number of qualities, skills, emotions, and feelings are listed in the center of this page and the next. If an item describes you better than it does many of your classmates, draw an arrow from that item to the "You" column on the left. If an item describes most of the people you know better than it describes you, draw an arrow from that item to the "Others" column on the right.

When you feel an item comes as close to describing you as it does the others in your group, draw arrows in both directions.

You   **Others**

honest

smile easily

willing to try something new

good sense of humor

intelligent

take pride in work

kind

forgive own mistakes

confident

generous

athletic

have lots of friends

usually happy

cooperative

YOU		OTHERS
	willing to share	
	lots of energy	
	enjoy life	
	good student	
	popular	
	easily frustrated	
	lonely	
	left out	
	often bored	
	forgive other people's mistakes	
	confused	
	sometimes afraid	
	like to compete	
	want to be best	
	tire easily	

Add five items of your own to complete this comparison.

_____

_____

_____

_____

_____

Now look back at the direction in which the arrows point. You probably see yourself as superior in some areas and not as well–off as many people in other instances.

That's what makes you the person you are. You're not like everyone, but you're not entirely different either.

Everyone Has Some Handicaps

More than ever before we are aware that many people have handicaps that affect their lives. We are used to seeing those with physical or mental handicaps and accept their differences. Perhaps you have such a handicap yourself.

There are things that might not normally be considered handicaps. For instance, poor eyesight is a real handicap in school, in sports, and in daily living until it is corrected with proper glasses. Lack of eye-hand coordination can be a handicap when doing physical things.

For similar reasons, severe allergies, major tooth problems, being greatly overweight, or having a bad heart may all prove to be physical handicaps.

We all have some sort of physical handicaps. Most aren't a major problem and we learn to deal with them.

What are two differences or problems you have to cope with that sometimes handicap you?

1. _____

2. _____

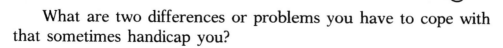

How do you deal with each of these physical differences so that the problems that result from them don't keep you from leading a good life?

1. _____

_____

2. _____

_____

Most of us have to deal with mental and emotional handicaps. A divorce often causes adjustment problems. An illness or injury that affects a family member or close friend can become an emotional handicap for other relatives or friends.

A parent out of work, living in a neighborhood you don't like, and fear of disease are all things that can cause mental or emotional handicaps.

What are two things in your life you might consider to be possible mental or emotional handicaps? After each item, describe briefly how you deal with it so it does not turn into a major problem.

1. _____

_____

_____

_____

2. _____

_____

_____

_____

Remember: All of us have handicaps of some sort. Some are visible to others; some are not. Living with these handicaps is part of life. Your personal handicaps may be different from those of your friends, but you're all alike in that you all have problems.

I Wish That . . .

What would you wish for if you had the chance? How would you change things if your wishes came true?

Imagine for a few minutes you have ten wishes to be granted. You cannot wish for money or for a physical item, however. This leaves out wishes for a million dollars or for a new mountain bike.

For what ten things would you wish?

1. _____

2. _____

3. _____

4. _____

5. _____

6. _____

7. _____

8. _____

9. _____

10. _____

Choose a partner from the members of your class. Compare your wish lists. How many wishes did the two of you make that were the same or almost the same?

_____

But I Want to Be Like Everyone Else

We've already talked about peer pressure. The desire to belong, to be like others, to be one of the group is a strong emotion. It's especially strong among children and youth because that's a time of life when we're trying to find where we fit into society.

We do and say things to cause others to see us as just like everyone else. Even though we're all different, it's quite normal to want to be just like those who are our friends or whose friendship we'd like to have.

More than likely, you've often found yourself trying to fit in and avoid seeming even slightly different from others. Briefly tell what you've done or been tempted to do in an attempt to be just like everyone else in regard to the following areas.

CLOTHING

_____

_____

_____

_____

SCHOOL WORK AND GRADES

_____

_____

_____

_____

LANGUAGE AND SPEECH

_____

_____

_____

_____

CHOICE OF FRIENDS

_____
_____
_____
_____

ACTIONS

_____
_____
_____
_____

OTHER AREAS

_____
_____
_____
_____

Smoking or chewing tobacco, drinking, and experimenting with drugs are often the result of a desire to be part of the gang or of a fear of being regarded as different, cowardly, or babyish.

Write five statements that you've heard others say (or you think they *could* say) to persuade people to begin using tobacco, alcohol, or illegal drugs.

1. _____

2. _____

3. _____

4. _____

5. _____

Whether you've used or been tempted to use tobacco, alcohol, or drugs is not an issue here. What is important is realizing that you can be different and still be accepted by good people everywhere.

Write a short answer that could be given in response to each of the five statements above and that would let others know it is not necessary to do what they ask in order to be accepted by others.

_____

_____

_____

_____

Friends Don't Rat on One Another

Most of your life you've been told not to be a tattletale. You've also been taught that reporting law breakers is part of being a good citizen.

Where does this leave you? When does reporting a wrongdoing make you a good citizen and when does it make you a tattletale? Since you're different from other people, you may not agree with even your best friend as to what should be reported and when. You may also disagree as to whom you should talk to about misdeeds you have witnessed or about which you have heard.

Your personal values, those of your family and friends, your neighborhood attitudes, and what you have experienced all have a lot to do with the way you react to crime and wrongdoing. The identity of the person in the wrong may also influence your actions.

Consider each of the following acts. Would you report the wrongdoer to a person in authority? (That can be your parent, a teacher, a shop keeper, the police, etc., depending upon the problem.) Mark the appropriate column after making your choice.

If you decide you would report the wrongdoer, tell why in the space provided. If your decision is not to report the problem, explain what you would do instead of reporting it. Add a few words telling why your choice is better than reporting the culprit.

	YES	*NO*
1. Your friend has just shoplifted a candy bar.	____	____
2. A seven-year-old boy has shoplifted a ball glove. He lives down the street, but you don't know his name.	____	____
3. The girl who always gets a better math grade than you do is cheating. You can see her crib notes on the floor beside her foot.	____	____
4. One of the toughest guys in the neighborhood has just stolen an old woman's purse. He knows you saw him.	____	____
5. Your best friend's sister just bought marijuana from the dealer who's been hanging around the school. She gets caught if you report him.	____	____
6. Your parents are openly cheating on their income tax returns.	____	____
7. You're pretty certain your minister is having sexual contact with several young boys in the church.	____	____

	Yes	*No*

8. You got the license number of the hit-and-run driver as she sped away from the child she had hit in the school crossing.   ____ ____

_____

9. For the third time in a week, you see the great-looking kid you'd hoped to date ripping off your employer at the place you both work part-time.   ____ ____

_____

10. The drunk next door is beating his wife and kids just as he does every weekend.   ____ ____

_____

Death and Dying

Few of us enjoy talking about death. It isn't something seen just on the movie screen or on TV. It's real. It's permanent. And it's frightening.

Some deaths come without warning. An auto accident, an apartment fire, or a random shooting can bring death so suddenly that no one has time to prepare for the loss.

Other deaths are expected. Old age, failure to recover from an accident, a mugging or an assault, or disease all give us time to consider death and prepare ourselves for the event.

The shock of sudden death is tremendous. Waiting for an expected death can be terrible. We all react in different ways to these tragic events.

Disbelief is a normal first reaction to death, whether it is unexpected or foretold. This feeling is summed up with words such as "This can't be! It isn't true!"

A second common reaction is to search for the reason this has happened or is going to occur. Why did he have to die? What did she do wrong? Why me? are the sorts of questions that are often asked.

Anger often follows. "It isn't fair! She's a good person. Look at all the rotten individuals who go on living!" Words to this effect are spoken as a result of what seems an unfair situation.

When death is foreseen, many people try to bargain after they get over their anger. Some pray for life and good health and offer to do certain things in return. Others try to convince their doctors that they will survive by doing exactly what is necessary.

Depression sets in when people realize they or their loved ones are beyond recovery. It is common to feel bad about things that won't ever be done.

Eventually, whether in the case of sudden death or a death to come, we realize it can't be changed. This is called *acceptance* and means simply that death is a part of life and comes to us all.

How you feel about death has a lot to do with how you've been raised and your experiences with death.

Take the following personal survey to help you understand a bit more about your feelings toward death. Place a check mark in front of the answer or answers that best describe your thoughts and experiences.

1. How did your family talk about death?

_____ Out in the open

_____ Only when absolutely necessary

_____ Never

2. How was death described to you?

_____ People go to heaven if they have been good.

_____ Death is like taking a trip.

_____ It's like going to sleep.

_____ Some other explanation

3. What was your first personal experience with death?

_____ A grandparent

_____ A parent

_____ A relative

_____ A family friend

_____ A pet

4. If you learned you had just six months to live, what would you want to do?

_____ Have as many new experiences as possible.

_____ Try to live a better life.

_____ Go on with what you have been doing.

_____ Quit school because it won't do any good.

5. We accept tears as a part of grief after death of a loved one. Why do we cry at the time of death and afterwards?

_____ We feel sorrow for the one who died.

_____ The one who dies has been cheated.

_____ Our personal loss is great.

_____ We're afraid of what life will be like without them.

6. Suicide is a leading cause of death among youth and young adults. What might cause someone your age to take his or her own life?

       _____ To hurt someone else
       _____ Fear
       _____ Loneliness
       _____ Disgrace
       _____ Death of a loved one
       _____ A disease such as AIDS
       _____ Family problems

7. Because of severe injury or incurable disease, some people are beyond the power of doctors to cure. What should be done in these cases?

       _____ They should be treated until death comes.
       _____ If they wish, a doctor should end their life painlessly.
       _____ When they wish, treatment should end and they should be allowed to die on their own.
       _____ Family members should have treatment stopped when there is no hope and the patient is not able to act on his or her own.
       _____ Doctors should decide when further treatment is a waste of time and money.

8. If you were given the power, which of the following would you choose?

       _____ Death would be unexpected.
       _____ Death would come when I'm still healthy and enjoying life.
       _____ I'd die when extremely old no matter how healthy.
       _____ I'd like advance warning in order to say good-bye and get my affairs in order.

I'm Different in My Own Way

By now you realize just how much you are like others and in which ways you differ from them. You have a good idea what makes you the person you are. At the same time, you should realize that it is a combination of samenesses and differences that cause you to be your own person.

How are you like your family and friends? How are you different?

Your basic roots come from your family. You are going to fill out the tree on the next page in order to show the ways in which you are different and the same as those around you. In the roots of the tree, list the ways you are like your parents and other family members.

As you grow, you learn from friends, teachers, neighbors, and others in the world. In the trunk of the tree, list various ways you are just like the people around you.

Though you are like others, you are different in a number of ways. In the tree's branches, list these differences that help make you the unique, wonderful person you are.

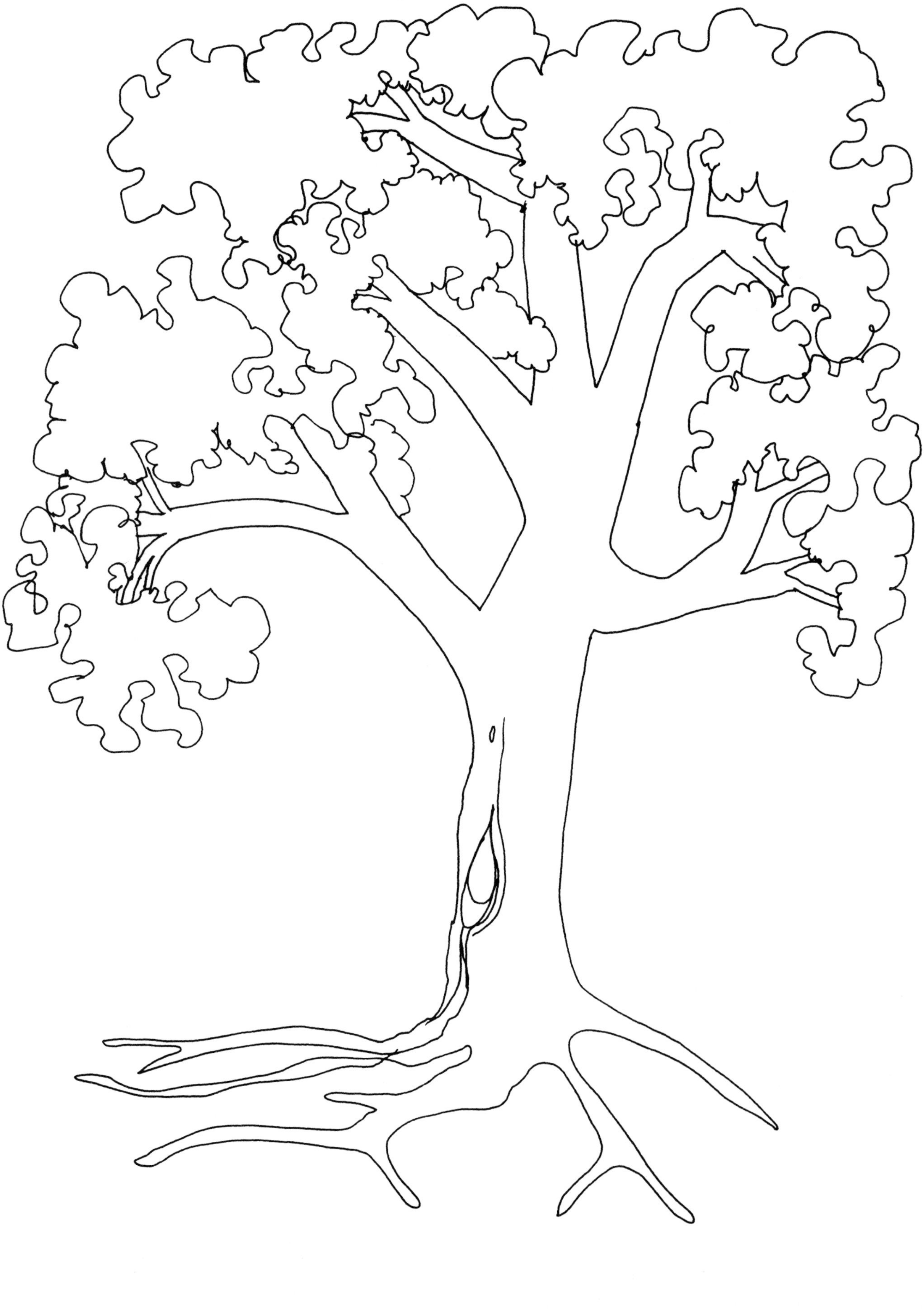

6
Who I Want to Be

How many times have you been asked, "What do you want to be when you grow up?"

A far more important question—one to ask yourself—is, "*Who* do I want to be?"

No one can accurately predict the future. Too many unexpected things happen in life to make a completely accurate prediction possible. At the same time, we must *anticipate* the future. We all have to set our eyes on distant goals and work toward them.

You've already set some short-term goals and checked to see how many of them you have reached. Now look ahead and think about the goals you still need to reach to become the person you'd like to be.

Long-Term Goals

When you think about setting a long-term goal, you may be considering something a month, a year, or perhaps ten years in the future. It is a great feeling to eventually reach a long-term goal.

Be sure to set realistic long-term goals. If your goals are too far out of reach, you'll feel frustrated or defeated when you don't reach them. Deciding now to go to college is a long-term goal that can most likely be met. Vowing today you'll become an Olympic gold-medal winner is a goal few people can meet.

There's nothing wrong with deciding to improve your athletic ability and work toward making the Olympic team. At the same time, you need to realize only a limited few of all the world's athletes win gold medals. In this instance, improved athletic ability is a worthwhile goal you can achieve. The gold medal is the stuff dreams are made of. It's great to dream. If you happen to be one of the gifted few with gold medal ability, then set your sights high. Just don't set impossible goals that will lead you to eventually view yourself as a failure when the goals can't be met.

Let's take a few minutes to discover how to tell if a long-term goal is a reasonable goal.

First, any goal you set has to be one you can define. It has to be definite. It's all fine to decide you want to improve. But self-improvement has to be specific to become a long-term goal. Decide exactly what sort of self-improvement you plan. Put it into exact words. Then it can become a goal.

Secondly, goals have to be reasonable. Do you really believe you can read three 400-page books for extra English credit before tomorrow night?

A third thing to consider in setting long-term goals is whether they can actually be reached. If you currently jog two miles per day, three days each week, is it reasonable to set a goal of jogging fifteen miles daily beginning today?

Be sure the goals you set can be identified when you've reached them. If you plan to increase the weight you bench press by ten pounds, you'll know when you've met that goal.

Another thing to think about in setting goals is whether *you* really want to do what you're considering. Do you want to swim fifty laps daily or is it something your mother wants because she always wanted to be a championship swimmer but never had the chance?

Finally, set goals that won't hurt you or others. Is winning the class election important enough to justify lying about other candidates, threatening those who might vote against you, and bribing someone to fake the ballot count?

These basic ideas concerning goals apply to any goals you set. Since we're looking toward the future, how about checking out a long-term goal against the six qualifications we have just covered.

1. What is a goal you'd like to accomplish within the next month or so?

_____

_____

2. What makes this goal reasonable?

_____

3. Why do you feel you can reach this goal?

_____

4. How will you know when you've reached your goal?

_____

5. Why set this particular goal?

_____

_____

_____

6. In working toward this goal, are there any potentially harmful things you need to watch out for?

_____

_____

_____

All that's left now is to work toward accomplishing the goal you have just outlined.

I've Already Come a Long Way

It's often hard to realize just how far you've come along the road toward becoming the person you want to be. This is because you're caught up in the day-to-day process of living. You're constantly growing and changing but may not be aware of just how much you've grown and changed.

Sometimes it helps to look back in order to compare where you are now with where you have been.

Pick a time in the past (say six months or even a year ago) and itemize some of the changes and growth that have taken place during that period of time. Just to keep you feeling human, it's a good idea to consider a few of the negatives as well as all the positives. We don't grow and improve steadily. It's often a process of a success or two, a disappointment, another success, perhaps a failure, then several more successes.

1. What is the starting period in the past that I'm going to use to compare myself with the present?

   _____

   _____

2. How have I changed physically since then?

   _____

   _____

3. What three good things happened during that time?

   _____

   _____

4. What did I learn in my favorite class during that time?

   _____

   _____

5. Did I forget something or become less skilled at something during that time? What?

_____

_____

6. What new responsibilities did I accept during that period?

_____

_____

7. Did I acquire more privileges during that time? What are they?

_____

_____

8. Was I disappointed over something important to me?

_____

_____

9. In what area did I make the most improvement?

_____

_____

10. How did I grow or change in one area not already mentioned above?

_____

_____

Life Is to Be Enjoyed

Planning for tomorrow, for next week, for next year, and even ten years in advance is important. You just can't drift through life without planning for the future.

But what about now? What about today?

Don't forget to get the most out of every day of your life. Future planning is necessary, but enjoying today is just as important. You don't want to focus so completely on the future that you lose sight of the good things in life you enjoy every day.

Take a few minutes to consider the good things in your life, right now, today, that help make the day enjoyable for you.

What good things are going on in your life that make this a good day for you?

Tell about something happening in your family that helps you enjoy this day.

_____

_____

_____

What's going on among your friends that makes this a day you can really enjoy?

_____

_____

_____

Things at school are sometimes great or good. Sometimes they are less than wonderful. Life's like that. Describe some of the things at school that make this a good day for you.

_____

_____

_____

Other things help make days enjoyable. Perfect weather can make a good day great or a so-so day better. A happy news item can help you enjoy a day. An announcement, a bit of success or a reward, or an invitation all help you to enjoy certain days. What's happened today in any of these areas to make the day a happy day for you?

_____

_____

Almost every day has something good about it, even though you may think of the day as nothing special—or even a bad day. What's the single best thing about today?

_____

_____

_____

Looking Toward My Future

Goals give meaning to life. Setting goals you can reach is one way to direct the course of your life. Take time now to look to your future. What are some goals you can set today that may help you become the sort of person you'd like to be?

It's easy to come up with a multitude of worthy goals. But it's hard—even impossible—to reach many goals at once. Instead of thinking about twenty or thirty great goals for your future, how about considering three long-term goals? These may be goals you hope to reach in a few months, a year, five years, or even longer.

As you think about these goals, keep in mind the six things you dealt with earlier (page 143) in regard to setting goals you can achieve.

What are three reasonable long-term goals you can set now that will help you become who you want to be? How long will it take to reach each goal you set?

1. _____

_____

_____

2. _____

_____

_____

3. _____

_____

_____

Why is each goal you've just set a worthwhile goal toward which you should work?

1. _____

_____

2. _____

_____

3. _____

_____

In what ways, other than any you may have mentioned above, will meeting each of these goals help you grow into the person you want to become?

1. _____

   _____

2. _____

   _____

3. _____

   _____

It's one thing to set a great goal. It's another to reach that goal. What may hinder you or slow you down as you work toward these three goals?

1. _____

   _____

2. _____

   _____

3. _____

   _____

The Road Toward Your Future Isn't Always Smooth

Some roads are smooth and straight. Others are rough or full of curves and hazards. Sometimes detours spring up and require us to take an alternate road.

This is just as true of the road toward your future as it is of highways. Just as it helps to plan a cross–country drive, it helps to plan for your future.

Begin with reasonable goals that are worthy of your efforts. Consider possible road blocks and detours. Then give a little thought to possible alternate routes you may take if your original goal proves impossible or less important than you first thought.

Sometimes it helps to diagram goals and potential hazards. To see how this works, complete the *goals road maps* on the next three pages. Set three goals that are different from the ones you just worked with on the previous page. Consider possible road blocks that may cause you to change your long-term goals. Try to anticipate the change necessary for each road block.

Begin by stating your goal on the main road. Give the completion date for reaching that goal at the end of the road.

List possible road blocks at each detour sign. Tell how you can change your plans to overcome these road blocks if they should appear.

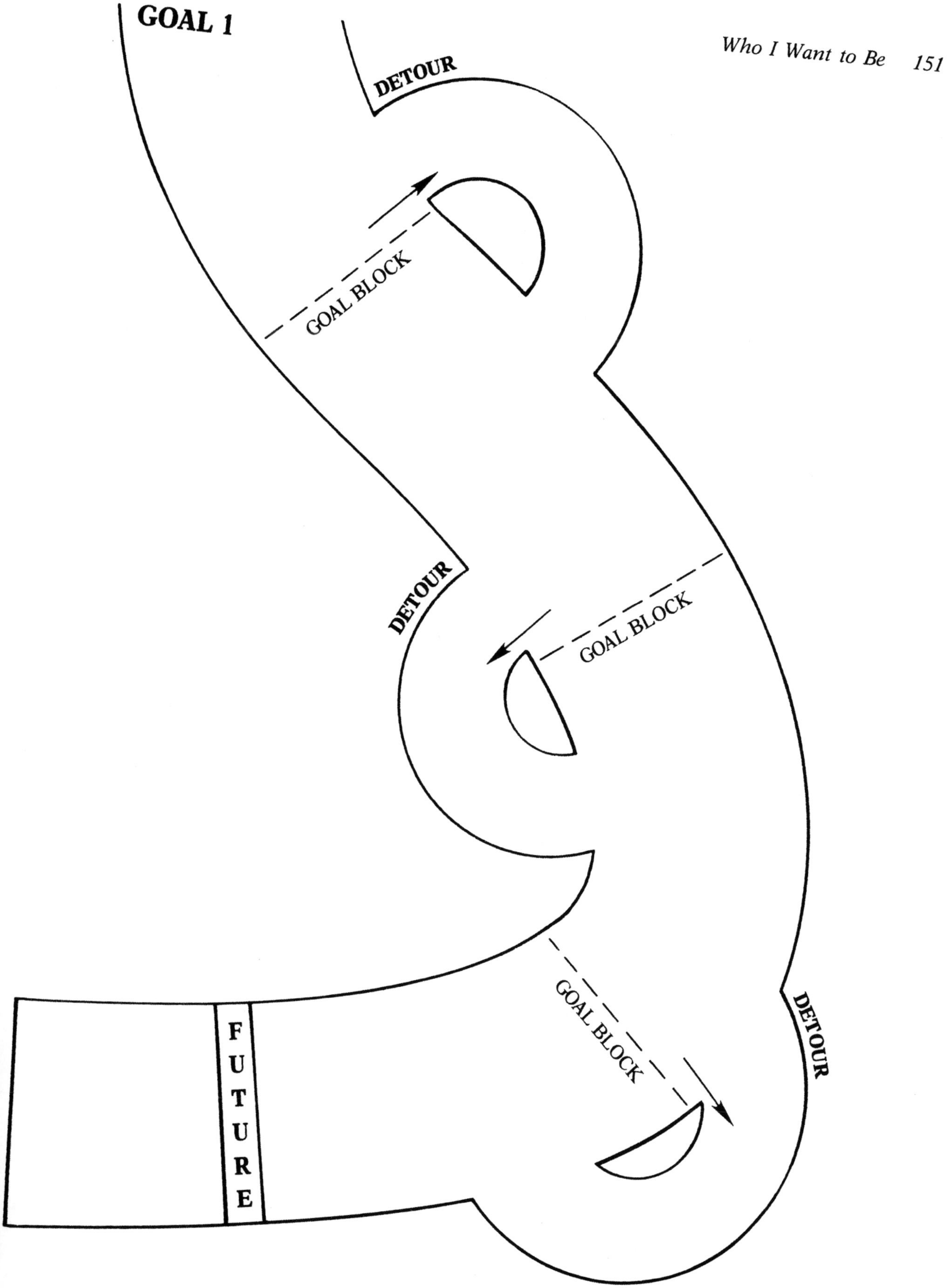

GOAL 1

DETOUR

GOAL BLOCK

DETOUR

GOAL BLOCK

GOAL BLOCK

DETOUR

FUTURE

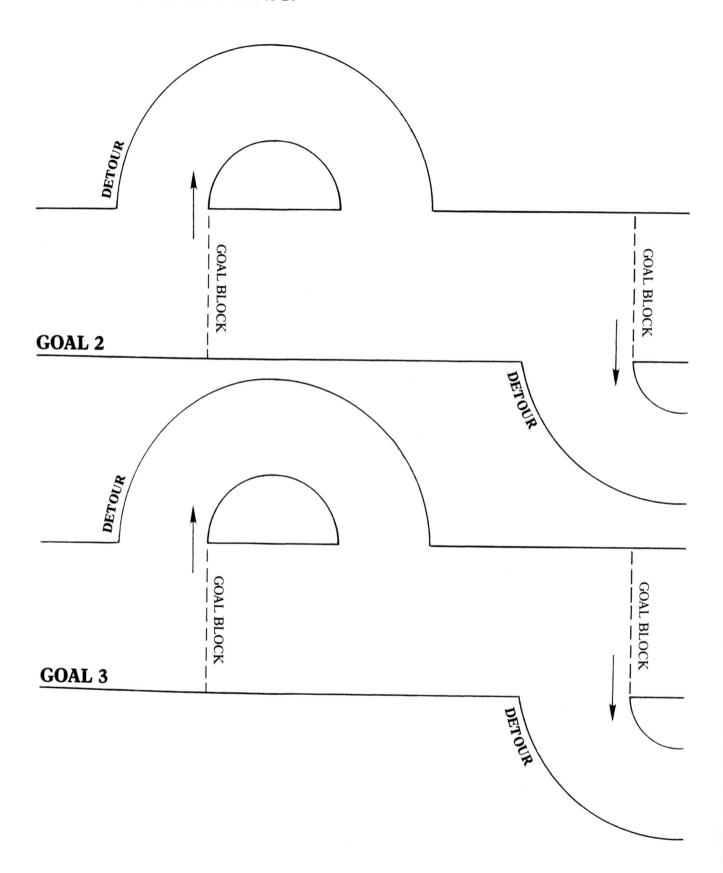

GOAL 2

DETOUR

GOAL BLOCK

GOAL BLOCK

GOAL 3

DETOUR

DETOUR

GOAL BLOCK

GOAL BLOCK

DETOUR

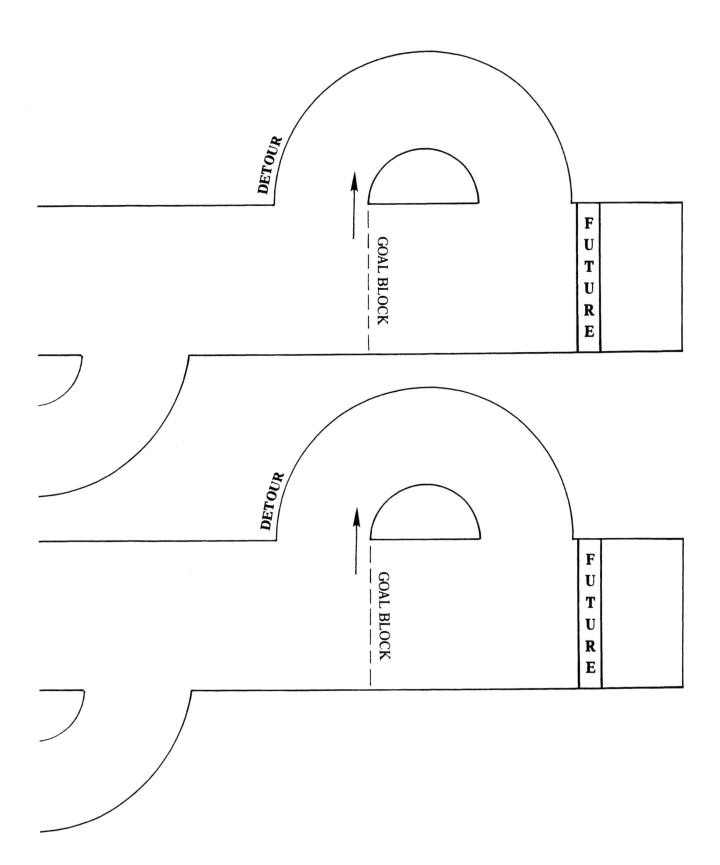

What I Believe About Life

We all believe certain things about life. These beliefs have a lot to do with the way we live. Read each of the following statements. Decide whether or not you accept that statement as correct for you. Mark the appropriate column for each statement.

	ACCEPT	*DON'T ACCEPT*
1. My past is what makes me the person I am now.	____	____
2. I should always do what makes me feel good.	____	____
3. Unless I do my best in all things, I'm not a good person.	____	____
4. I'm better off doing only those things at which I am good and feel comfortable doing.	____	____
5. All those who care for me and who are important to me should accept me the way I am.	____	____
6. When things don't go my way, I am hurt.	____	____
7. I get upset over other people's problems.	____	____
8. It isn't a good idea to care too much for others, because then I may get hurt.	____	____
9. I spend time worrying over bad things that may happen some day.	____	____
10. I expect things to go well for me in the years ahead.	____	____

Now that you've reacted to those statements, write five short statements that tell what you believe about life.

1. _____

_____

2. _____

_____

3. _____

_____

4. _____

_____

5. _____

_____

I'm Becoming a Stronger, Better Person

We all have weaknesses and we all have strengths. One way to improve our lives and the way we see ourselves is to learn to turn our weaknesses into strengths.

Pumping iron improves muscle strength. Aerobic exercise such as cycling, swimming, walking, or jogging helps improve the cardiovascular system which results in better circulation and lung capacity.

Recognizing personal weaknesses and working to turn them into strengths improves our quality of life.

The first step in turning weakness to strength is recognizing a weak point. For example, arriving late to class is a weakness.

Not only does this irritate your teachers, it also gives others a poor impression of you. Making it to class on time erases this weakness and makes you a stronger person.

Refusing to wear your glasses leaves you weaker because of the difficulty in seeing properly. You're a stronger person when you put them on and see what's happening in the world.

Look at yourself. You're a good person. But even good people can become stronger and better people.

In order to overcome weaknesses, you must first recognize them. You must also *want* to change. Finally, you have to be willing to take the necessary steps in order to change.

Can you identify five personal weaknesses you'd like to change? Then can you come up with some practical steps that will help you grow out of each weakness?

Every time you overcome a weakness, you're stronger for having done so.

WEAKNESSES I'D LIKE TO CHANGE	HOW TO MAKE THE CHANGE
1. _____	_____
	_____
	_____
2. _____	_____
	_____
	_____
3. _____	_____
	_____
	_____

WEAKNESSES I'D LIKE TO CHANGE	*HOW TO MAKE THE CHANGE*
4. _____	_____
	_____
	_____
5. _____	_____
	_____
	_____

How Do I Know When I'm Successful?

We talk about success. We want to be successful. Just how do you know when you've finally achieved success?

Success means different things to different people. To some, success is achieved only when they make large sums of money. To others, having a happy family life is a sign of sure success.

What does being successful mean to you? What do you have to accomplish in order to feel you are a success? How do you know when you're a success?

Use the space below and on the following page to write a short paragraph or two in which you sum up your feelings about personal success. What is it, what do you have to do to be a success, and how can you judge your own success?

_____

_____

_____

_____

_____

_____

_____

_____

_____

_____

_____

_____

_____

_____

Racing Toward My Future

Your future is a goal toward which you work. It's not as easy to see as is the finish line in a race. Unlike a finish line, the future keeps moving away from you. Once you reach a point in the future, you'll always have more future ahead of you. That's a great thing about your life and future. There's always future for which you can plan and hope.

Think of your life as the six-lane track below. Each lane represents a different and important part of your life. At this very moment, you're at the starting line. The finish line is five years from now.

The question is, what do you expect to have accomplished when you reach the finish line five years in the future? Write your future goals in the space at the finish line.

Between the starting line (today) and the finish (five years from now), note the steps you'll take and the things you plan to accomplish as you race toward the future along each lane.

START	*FINISH*
Education	
Family and Friends	
Emotional and Mental Growth	
Physical Growth	
Work, Job, and Career	
Other	

Moving Toward Who I Want to Be

In the past days and weeks, you've taken a good look at who you are. You know more about why you are the person you are than you did when you began this book. By now you have considered who it is you wish to be. You've probably got some sound ideas concerning what you need to do in the days, months, and years ahead in order to develop into the person you wish to become.

Some people call this *climbing life's ladder*. The idea behind considering life as climbing a ladder is that each time you move forward, each time you make an advance, you're actually climbing higher toward your eventual goal.

Think of who you want to be as a shelf containing many items. These might be labeled *a good parent, a successful lawyer, a kind person, an honest individual,* or any of the goals you're now setting for yourself.

Think of the growth you're going to make in future years as a ladder between you and the items on the shelf. What steps are you planning in the future to help you become the person you've decided upon becoming? One step might be *graduating from high school* while another may well be *marrying someone I love and who loves me.*

Label the items on the shelf with what you want to do and become when you become the person you wish to be.

Label the ladder steps and spaces between the steps with those things you plan to do to help you become that special person you want to be.

As the months and years go by, remember this final picture from time to time. Keep in mind your hopes and goals. Always remember that even when things go wrong, you are a good person with a bright future.

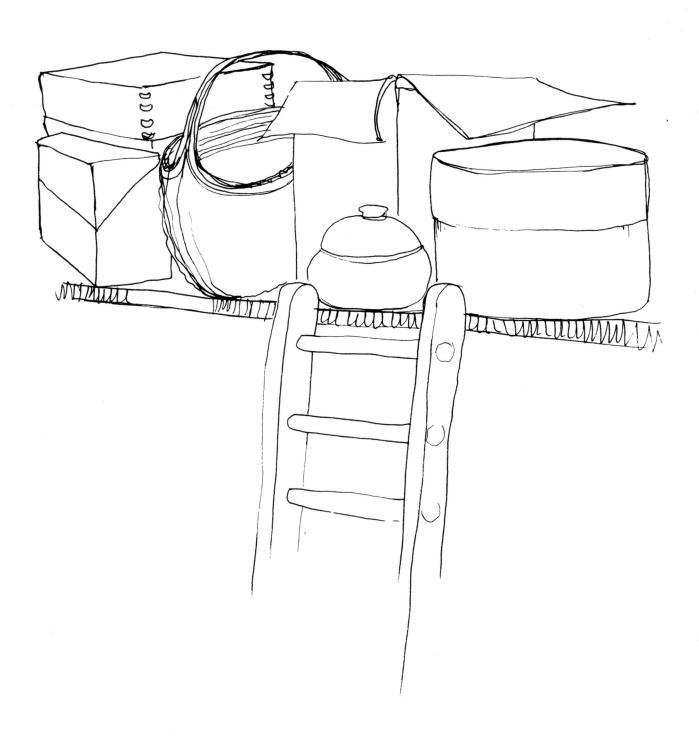